Andrea Levy was born in ⬚⬚⬚⬚⬚⬚⬚⬚⬚⬚ parents. She is the author of *Every Light in the House Burnin'*, *Never Far from Nowhere*, *Fruit of the Lemon* and *Small Island*, all of which were critically acclaimed. She is a recipient of an Arts Council Writer's Award and winner of the 2004 Orange Prize for Fiction, the 2004 Whitbread Novel Award, the 2004 Whitbread Book of the Year, the 2005 Commonwealth Writers' Prize Best Book Award and the 2005 Orange Prize for Fiction Best of the Best. Andrea lives and works in London.

Praise for *Every Light in the House Burnin'*:

'A rich and colourful portrait. The only disappointment is that . . . it ends' *Literary Review*

'An interesting and touching book' *Daily Telegraph*

'You won't be able to put this book down' *Pride*

'Levy's skill and cunning leave the reader shaken' *The Voice*

'Andrea Levy is the long-awaited birdsong of one born black and gifted in Britain. Let her sing and sing' Marsha Hunt

'Consistently moving' *The Sunday Times*

'Funny, lucid, quirky and touching, it held me to the last page. Andrea Levy is a fresh and invigorating new voice' Ferdia Mac Anna, author of *The Last of the High Kings*

'Stands comparison with some of the best stories about growing up poor – humorous and moving, unflinching and without sentiment' *Independent on Sunday*

'An extremely powerful novel, a striking and promising debut' *TLS*

ANDREA LEVY

EVERY LIGHT IN THE HOUSE BURNIN'

headline
review

First published in 1994 by REVIEW

First published in paperback in 2004 by REVIEW

This special edition published in paperback in 2006
by HEADLINE REVIEW

An imprint of Headline Book Publishing

1

ISBN 0 7553 3076 5

Printed and bound in Great Britain by
Clays Ltd, St Ives plc

Headline's policy is to use papers that are natural, renewable and
recyclable products and made from wood grown in sustainable
forests. The logging and manufacturing processes are expected to
conform to the environmental regulations of the country of origin.

HEADLINE BOOK PUBLISHING
A division of Hodder Headline
338 Euston Road
London NW1 3BH

www.reviewbooks.co.uk
www.hodderheadline.com

To my Dad, my Mum and Bill

Chapter 1

My dad once drank six cups of tea and ate six buttered rolls. Not in the course of a day, which would be nothing unusual. No, he drank six cups of tea and ate six buttered rolls one after the other to avoid them being wasted.

It happened in a motorway café where we had stopped on our coach journey down to Devon. It was the first holiday I had ever taken in my life. I was eleven. We all went, my mum and dad, my two sisters and my brother. Our destination was a Pontin's holiday camp in Brixham. When we stopped at the motorway café we had all wanted various items from the display of food. 'Fish and chips please, Dad,' I said hopefully. 'Cake and cola please,' from my sister. We had never been out with our dad for a meal before so we had no idea what his response would be.

My dad sucked his teeth and jangled loose change around in his pocket as he looked at the prices on the menu. Then he ordered six cups of tea and six buttered rolls. We were all disappointed.

We sat watching my dad slurp at his tea with relish and shower his suit with crumbs from the roll. It was us and him. One by one, with our roll and tea in front of us we said we didn't feel hungry any more. My dad looked surprised at first. 'Eat up,' he encouraged with a mouthful of bread. But then resigned himself as he made us all pass the items down to him. My mum was the last. She looked embarrassed, sitting at a table with a man who had five cups of tea and five plates of rolls around him, which he was systematically devouring. She said she had to go to the toilet and left to get back on the coach.

The humiliation did not stop there. Because my dad finished every last item, he was late getting back to the coach. The driver paced up to us to ask where he was. One of the other passengers said he was still eating in the café. We all waited with people tutting and staring at us. Then my dad emerged from the toilets at the side of the café. He was running. He smiled at everyone as he walked to his seat but nobody smiled back. He sat down and we were off.

MY DAD

My dad was a man – most dads are. But my dad had been taught or was shown or picked up that a man was certain things and a woman was others. I don't know whether he ever questioned the assumptions but I can identify him now as a man thought up in the 1930s and 40s.

He was head of a family – a breadwinner. He should go out to work in the morning and come home at night. He had to discipline children and occasionally do things around the home that required some degree of physical strength. A man did not have to be loving and affectionate. A man had to know everything and never be seen not to understand the world. A man would help around the house only when asked but a man always emptied the bins.

My dad was a man and he did what he thought was expected of him. But he couldn't understand when more was demanded.

'What!' he'd say if he had to take any of us to the dentist. 'What!' if expected to attend a school function. 'Cha,' if expected to wash up. And 'Oh my God!' if my mum ever announced that she would not be in so he'd have to look after us.

My dad was from Jamaica – born and bred. He came to this country in 1948 on the *Empire Windrush* ship. My mum joined him six months later in his one room in Earl's Court. He never talked about his family or his life in Jamaica. He seemed only to exist in one plane of time – the present. There is an old photo of him – grainy black and white that shows him dressed in an immaculate tailored suit with wide baggy trousers, wearing a shirt with a collar held by a pin, and a proper tie. His hair is short and well groomed. He is standing by a chair in the grounds of what looks to be a beautiful house. The photo looks like my dad as a 'Great Gatsby'-type millionaire. When I asked my dad about the photo that fascinated me, he would grudgingly admit that it was where he lived. But when I pressed him to tell me more he would shrug and tell me not to bother him. Or he'd suck his teeth and ask me why I was interested. He would ask this in the manner of somebody who does not want an answer – of somebody who would like you to leave them alone.

My dad had a job with the Post Office. He'd been in the same job for as long as I knew him. But I couldn't tell you what he did or who he did it with. I'm afraid I can't tell you if he enjoyed his work – if he longed to go every day because it brought him fulfilment and happiness – or whether he dreaded every morning and watched the clock until he could leave. I can't tell you because I don't know. My dad was a man and men didn't talk about their work. It was a secret between him and his wage packet. If you asked him what he did at work, he'd shrug and say that he worked for the Post Office.

My dad called my mum 'Mum' and my mum called my dad 'Dad'. I was about ten years old before I knew their actual names – Winston and Beryl. My dad didn't like anyone to know his name. It was another secret. If we said

3

it in public he would look embarrassed and tell us not to say it again. And if we said it too loudly at home he would tell us to be quiet. As for my dad's age – well that was shrug-shoulders age, that was absolutely-none-of-my-business age, that was don't-bother-me age.

I should describe my dad – tell you what he looked like. But who would I describe? Should I describe the young man I knew with neatly greased-back wavy hair, who would throw me up in the air or ask to hold my hand when we crossed the road.

Or should I tell you about the pot-bellied middle-aged man who spent hours in front of the mirror trying to conceal his grey hair. Or perhaps I should describe the old, wild-haired man – fat and bloated by steroids aimed at keeping his dying body alive a little longer. My dad was all these men and many more. Some said he showed a resemblance to the late President Sadat of Egypt in his younger days. And he did sometimes – around the nose.

My dad was on the late shift at the Post Office – he started work at twelve noon and finished at eight o'clock at night. This shift meant, by accident or design, that he managed to avoid any prolonged contact with his family. He was never an early riser and would spend the frantic morning rush propped up in bed with a cigarette, the *Daily Mirror* and breakfast on a tray. He didn't get up until everyone was safely out.

In the school holidays I would sit with him during his two hours and watch his routine. He got up and made every bed in the flat, with the blank expression of a job performed but not remembered. He tugged at sheets, flattened blankets, plumped pillows until every bed was neat, ready for another night's sleep.

After this he'd neaten himself. He dressed in a suit every day. He didn't have many suits but the ones he did have were all the same. They all had wide baggy trousers with turn-ups at the bottom. They were all in shades of grey

4

and only my dad could tell the difference between them.

When he was dressed, my dad sat on the edge of the bed and polished his shoes. He dabbed some polish on the brush, then rubbed it furiously into the leather with a motion that shook his body and the bed. Then he buffed them until they shone.

He brushed his hair in the same way. Using a different brush and substituting polish for Brylcreem, he'd stroke every hair into place until he had a shiny black glaze on his head.

He would always wear a tie which he would knot without looking. Then lastly he'd put on his jacket and adjust the lapels with a strange pigeon-like movement of the neck, bobbing his head and straightening the fabric at the same time.

One day I refused to go to school – I wanted to stay home. I was about six years old and decided that going to school every day was unnecessary. My mum had long since given up trying to get me out and had gone to work. My dad was left with the job of persuading me to attend.

'You're going,' he said, 'as soon as I'm dressed.'

'No, I want to stay here with you,' I said.

'I'm going to work nuh man – cha, don't be silly.'

'I don't feel well – I'm not going,' I screamed.

Suddenly my dad leapt from his bed still in his pyjamas. He sprang at me like a tiger and grabbed my arm. I was terrified. All of a sudden he looked like no one I recognized. His face was contorted with anger – red and round.

'You want to stay with me in my castle,' he shouted into my face. 'It's so lovely here – you just want to stay with me here?'

Fear carried me out of the room and towards the front door. But my dad chased after me grabbing at my skirt and pulling me back.

'Come and stay in my castle,' he kept saying like some hideous fairy-story witch. His pyjamas were all dishevelled and his penis was poking through the gap in the pants. I screamed but he carried on dragging me back.

'Come to my castle. It's so lovely,' he kept repeating. I struggled from his grip then ran for the door. I managed to open it before he caught me and I ran out without looking back.

I didn't go back until the evening when my mum came home. I spent the day in refuge at my friend's house – her mother didn't go out to work. When I saw him that evening he smiled at me and handed me a pink hyacinth in a pot.

'A lady I know gave it to me,' he said. Then he rubbed my head and sat and watched television.

My older brother and sisters knew my dad's quick, fiery temper well. It didn't take much for them to provoke him into shouting 'Child' and jumping up from his seat with no regard to anything around him. Yelling 'Come here,' then grabbing at the buckle of the belt that ran through his trousers. With a deft movement he would whip the belt out from its loops – so fast that it could send him into a spin like a top. Then he'd beat them with the belt, following them where they ran or cowered. He'd bring the strap down on them shouting a word before each strike. 'Stop' whomp 'that' whomp 'you' whomp 'hear' whomp, until his temper cooled.

He used to hit at my pram when I was a baby. Striking it with his belt and yelling for me to stop crying. But I couldn't remember that. I'd only been told.

MY MUM

My mum was a teacher – a teacher of small children. She began her working career in Jamaica where she earned her own living. Then she married my dad and they decided to come to England to find 'better opportunity'.

6

My mum was a tall woman, taller than my dad but the years shrunk her down. She had a head of thick black hair, which waved and curled any way she pleased. My mum's nose was large and wide and her lips thick. But her skin was pale. In Jamaica, they sometimes wouldn't serve her in shops, thinking that she was white, or sometimes she'd get privileged treatment for exactly the same reason.

My mum joined my dad in his one room in London. But the English wouldn't let her teach. They said she had to retrain before she could stand before English children. My mum didn't have the money to retrain and she then became pregnant, so she took in sewing at home instead.

My mum had four children. Three within one year of each other – two girls, Yvonne and Patricia, then a boy, John. Four years later she had me, Angela. The council gave my mum and dad a flat – a temporary flat on an old thirties' red brick council estate. They said it was just until they found somewhere more suitable, but that was before I was born and I lived there until I was twenty-one.

She looked after her four children and one husband in the small three-bedroom flat. There was no garden and the only sources of heat were coal and electric fires.

My mum was always cold, she never warmed up. 'This country is coooold,' she would say. She'd sit so near the fire that her legs became permanently red and blotchy. And she never took her coat off – she would cook or wash or sit, all in her outside coat.

'Aren't you taking your coat off, Mum?'

'I will – when I warm up,' she'd say. She made all her four children wear layers and layers of clothes because she was 'coooold'.

When I was five and old enough to go to school, my mum decided she'd had enough of sewing and went back to college to become again what she always had been – a teacher. After three years of washing, cooking, college, feeding, homework, bed, washing, cooking, college, feeding, homework, bed, she got her diploma.

My mum was an educated woman and she wanted to do what educated people did. Listen to classical music, but we only played soul, Tamla Motown and pop – 'It's got no words, Mum, and no beat'. Have stimulating conversation – 'Shut up, Mum. I can't hear the telly'. Go to the theatre – 'What you wanna go out for, you can see everything you want on the television and it's free'. And to talk properly – 'Do what, Mum? Leave it out. I ain't talkin' like tha'!'

So my mum took an Open University degree in Humanities and Social Science. She watched the programmes in the early mornings then went to work to teach 'her' children. At night she went to the shops and bought food, then carried it home, always in two carrier bags, 'to balance meself up'. She made her family their evening meal, then went into her bedroom to study. The room was too small to hold a desk and chair. My mum sat on the edge of her bed and splayed her books out around her and read and wrote for her degree. In the summer she went to summer schools at universities and would come back with tales of the nice food she ate, the lovely rooms she studied in and the educated people she met. After several years she got a BA.

My mum then wanted to visit her relations in America and Jamaica. She needed a passport. They wouldn't let her have one. After thirty-eight years of living in Britain, teaching British children, paying British taxes, learning British ways, she wasn't British. She needed to apply and pay £200.

We had Sunday-best clothes in our family. Clothes you weren't allowed to wear any other day. And my mum dressed me in my finest Sunday best to go to church. Clean, white, knee-length socks with black patent shoes. A red dress my mum made from 'old remnants' of cloth, which had a white Peter Pan collar and a red sash that went round my waist and tied into a giant bow at the back. She pulled at my long hair and plaited it back so tight that there was no hope any would escape and show us up with its frizz. She tied a large white ribbon on the end of the plait and another she wove through the hair on the top of my head. She scrubbed my face with a flannel and gave me a pair of white gloves to put on. When I was finished she turned me round and said, 'What a way you look nice.' She stood back from me like an artist and folded her arms. 'What a way you look nice,' she said again with pride. 'Give me a kiss off the ol' neck.' She grabbed me and sniffed her lips and nose against my face.

My mum then got dressed in her Sunday best. A turquoise dress with matching turquoise coat. The suit was made from shiny fabric and she brushed it down hard with the clothes brush and picked at the tiny bobbles of fibre that had appeared on the shoulders and elbows. She put on white shoes and polished them with a cloth. Then she got down her hat box from the top of the wardrobe in the bedroom. She brought out a turquoise hat with a broad rim and black band with a pom-pom flower on the side. My mum then powdered her face. She had a little gold compact that held loose powder and a mirror. She dabbed a small pad onto the powder and wiped it round her screwed up face like she was washing it with a wet flannel. She rolled up her red lipstick and wiped some over her tightly pursed lips. The whole operation looked like a torture for her and took about thirty seconds. She then dabbed perfume behind each ear and on each wrist. Lastly she finished off by pulling on her clean white gloves.

'We're just the same, Mum,' I said, lifting up my gloved hands.

My dad never went to church. He preferred to lie in bed on Sunday mornings, and there was the ironing on Sunday nights. I was pleased to go with her – she looked so tall and proud on Sundays. Not like she did during the week when she'd spend days sewing up dresses at the Singer sewing machine, dressed in a wrap-over apron whose pattern had faded over the years, her stocking tops hanging down over her knees because she couldn't stand to have them in suspenders all day and it was 'too cold' to have nothing on your legs at all; when you could ask her for a hairpin and she'd feel around in her hair for a few minutes then produce one. My mum had short hair with no need for hairpins, so it was odd. For years I thought that she grew hairpins – that my mum's head was the source of all the hairpins in the world.

But on Sundays she went to church and I was her prized, scrubbed youngest child.

We went to St Luke's Church on the hill. The church was brown. Brown outside and brown inside – apart from the stained-glass windows which sprinkled coloured light down when the sun shone. The vicar stood by the door as we went in, handing out prayer and hymn books with one hand while pulling on a rope which rang the bell with the other. The vicar smiled at us and said, 'Good morning,' to my mum then pulled hard on my cheek with the hand that had just been emptied of the books. 'Hello, little one,' he said.

It was cold in the church, a chill cold that could pass through any vest. Everybody would walk a few feet into the church and shiver -usually at the same spot – at the top of the aisle just before the pews began. It was like a dance – the St Luke's shiver. My mum said it was something to do with coming into the house of God.

Everything hushed as you entered the church. People whispered to each other. My mum tried to step lightly so her shoes didn't make a clip-clopping noise on the floor. The bell that rang so loudly outside the church deadened to a dull thud inside.

There were long wooden pews. Brown wood. Hard. We sat on a pew near the aisle. There were brown plastic cushions on the floor in front of us for kneeling on when you prayed. And on the back of the seat in front was a ledge where we put the prayer and hymn books.

My mum sat straight-backed in the pew and looked ahead of her to the table with the cloth and the cross on, which was the altar. Then she closed her eyes for a few moments, then opened them and began adjusting her coat.

The service began when the organ boomed great fat chords. It was a sound like no other, that hit you not in the ears but squarely in the chest, and made you draw breath hard then sigh it away. Soon a little door opened at the side of the chancel steps and out came the red and white robed choir. They all held hymn books in front of them and sang as they walked to take their places on the pews either side of the chancel. Their colours looked stark and glamorous against the brown. Then all the congregation stood up and began to sing the hymn with the choir.

My mum held her book in front of her and sang with her head up. She had a sweet voice and the sound of it reminded me of bed times and bath times. But I didn't know which hymn everyone was singing. So I nudged my mum, who shrugged me off and carried on. I nudged her again harder. She looked down at me with a curious furrowed brow.

'What are you singing?' I asked. She crinkled her forehead even more. She couldn't hear me. 'What hymn are you singing?' I shouted as loud as I could.

My mum said, 'Sschh,' and flicked at me with her hand. Then she handed me her open hymn book and took my closed one. She pointed at the hymn.

I peered at the tiny writing on the page. I could read – that was no problem – but I had to go slowly and use my finger over big words. Then the choir and the congregation sang the chorus, 'Hallelujah! Hallelujah! Hallelujah!' and I could join in. I opened my mouth wide and sang 'Hallelujah' again. But everyone else had gone on to the next verse. I decided that if I sang 'Hallelujah!' for long enough, eventually everyone would get round to it again and I'd be singing the right thing. So I carried on singing, trying to follow the tune. My mum began to nudge me. Proud of me I thought, until I looked at her face. She scowled down at me and looked flushed.

'Sschh, child,' she said slowly and deliberately.

I stopped singing and looked around me. Then everyone stopped and sat down on the pews. The vicar was now standing in the pulpit high above us. The pulpit had a large, brown wooden eagle carved on it and the outspread wings of the eagle held a large book – the Bible.

Then the vicar began to speak from the pulpit and he went on and on and on and on. I caught a few words that I understood – children – sin – Julie. My mum and the other adults laughed occasionally and I sat up thinking we'd got to a funny bit. But he just went on and on and on some more.

I looked round the church and saw a girl I knew from school. She was sitting in her white Sunday best a few rows behind me. I waved. She went to wave back but her mum nudged her and she returned to sitting still and silent, only giving me a little smile. I looked at the stained-glass windows and wondered what Jesus was pointing at and why He had great rings round His head. I looked at the choir and wondered why most of them were sitting with their heads down like you do when you're reading or playing 'hang man'. I looked at the brown beams high in the ceiling and wondered if any angels or birds lived up there.

The seat became so hard that my backside couldn't bear to be pressed against it any more. I had to stand up. But as I did my mum pulled the hem of my dress and yanked me back onto the pew. As soon as she let go I stood up again. My mum pulled me down again and held me there with her large hand firmly wrapped over my leg. And the vicar went on.

I swung my legs and looked at the vicar – why did he wear a dress? And why were the choir dressed in Arsenal colours? Did they all support Arsenal?

At last the vicar stopped talking and my mum slid off the pew and knelt on the cushion in front of her. I heard her knees crack as she went down. Then I heard knees cracking all over the congregation and a faint 'Oohh' coming from around. I knelt down but I found myself in a horrible dark space at the back of the pew. I couldn't see anything and I had nothing to hold on to. I stood up again and I was the same height as my mum. I could look her straight in the eyes.

'Look, Mum, I'm the same height as you.' I put my hand to my head and then to my mum's to show her what I meant.

'Okay, child – now kneel down,' my mum whispered to me.

'It's dark down there, Mum,' I said.

'Well, just stand there and be quiet nuh.' My mum spoke quickly in a whisper.

'What's happening now, Mum?' I said. I heard someone in the congregation laugh. As I looked round I noticed everyone was staring at me. Some were smiling, some not. 'Everyone's looking at me, Mum.'

'Sschh,' my mum said and hit me gently on the knee with her hand.

The vicar started to sing by himself. It wasn't like a hymn but a strange chanting sound. When he had finished the congregation started to chant back. Then the vicar went again. And then the congregation. At last a good game. I decided to sing with the vicar, to help him out. I sang my 'Hallelujah' as the vicar sang. My mum flicked at

13

my leg hard as she chanted the reply. When she stopped singing she turned and looked at me and gave me the look that stopped all 'horse-play' at home. The look that said 'it will end in tears'. The look that always made someone shout, 'It's not my fault.'

Then she whispered to me, 'Just wait till I get you home.'

When she began singing again I said, 'Can we go now then, Mum?'

'In a minute, child,' my mum hushed.

'Why can't we go now?' I asked.

'Don't argue,' she said slowly through her teeth.

'Well don't "arg" me then,' I shouted.

My mum suddenly bounced on to her feet. I had never seen her move so quickly. She grabbed me by my arm holding me by my armpit. She almost lifted me into the air. My legs were still on the ground but I hardly had to make any movement to walk. She pulled me from the pew, then down the aisle. My mum smiled at everyone as she moved past the pews as if nothing unusual was really happening. I smiled back at her but as she opened the church door her smile dropped.

'You show me up,' she said. 'Cha child – you show me up in front of everyone with your cheek.' I thought she'd put me down but she dragged me by the arm all the way home muttering, 'I'm not taking you again, you hear – I'm not taking you again!'

MY BROTHER

'That's disgusting – that can't be true. Mum and Dad wouldn't do anything so disgusting!'

'Well, how do you think babies are made then?'

'I don't know exactly, but I know it's nothing to do with that. That's not how it's done at all!'

14

'It is, stupid.'

''S not – who told you anyway?'

'I know. I know these things.'

My brother was usually right about everything. He was four years older than me and knew a lot more. I shared a bedroom with him. My sisters were in another room but there wasn't enough space for me and they didn't want me.

My brother was born with red hair – a red, fuzzy head of hair that people would stare at in the street. 'It's the Scottish in you,' my mum would say to him but she never explained where the Scottish came from. My brother lived in a secret world. He went out and nobody knew where he went or who he went with. 'Just going to see a man about a dog,' he would say if you asked him where he was going, and if you asked him where he had been he'd shrug and say, 'Been to see a man about a dog.' So I had to share a bedroom with my brother but I liked it.

At night we'd lie in bed and play games, like 'A to Z', where you'd choose a category – say girls' names, then you'd have to think of as many names as you could, going through the alphabet until you ran out. Sometimes we'd just talk until we fell asleep or one of us said, 'I'm going to sleep now.'

'When I grow up – you know, leave school – I'm going to be a motor racing driver,' my brother would start. My brother was dead keen on motor racing. Jim Clarke was his favourite and he was very upset when he died. Jackie Stewart was no consolation. 'I'm going to be world motor racing champion.'

'How you going to do that?' I'd ask.

'I've got plans.' My brother always had plans.

'Well, I'm going to be Julie Andrews.'

'You can't be Julie Andrews.'

'Why not?'

'Cause Julie Andrews is Julie Andrews!'

'Yeah, I know – but I'm going to be like her – sing and act in films.'

'You can't sing.'

'I can.'

'You can't.'

'I'll get lessons.'

'Who'd want you in a film?'

'I'll get discovered by some film director.'

'You won't – what film director's gonna come round 'ere?'

'He might. He might be driving through in his Rolls Royce or something and spot me. That's how it happens, you know.'

'It doesn't.'

'It does.'

'Doesn't.'

'It can – I've read it.'

'You can't act.'

'I can.'

'You can't.'

'I bet I could act like that dumb girl in that film *Mandy*. I could do that.' My brother would laugh. He always laughed.

'Well it's better than stupid motor racing.'

'Yeah, but I can do that.'

'You can't even drive.'

'All right, I'll bet you. I bet you I become six times world motor racing champion before you become Julie Andrews.'

'How much?'

'I bet you sixpence.'

'All right.'

'Right.'

But on this night the conversation had taken a different turn. My brother started sheepishly. 'D'you know how a woman gets pregnant?'

'Yeah, of course,' I lied.

'How?'

'Well, she kisses someone and . . .' I was stuck so I said, 'I'm not telling you.'

My brother laughed. 'You don't know,' he said emphatically.

'Well, how then if you're so clever?'

My brother didn't answer.

'You don't know yourself, see,' I said.

'I do,' he said, but he didn't go on.

'Well, I'm going to sleep now,' I said and settled back on my pillow.

'D'you wanna know?' he said after a pause. I didn't answer. Then he said quietly, 'The man puts his thing in the woman's hole.'

'What?' I said.

'The man puts his willie in the woman's hole – then the woman gets pregnant.'

It took me a little while to understand what he said. Then I began to get a picture in my mind and said, 'Of course they don't! Urghh, that's not how it's done at all. Urghh, that's disgusting. Nobody would do that!'

'It's true – that's how it's done.'

'It's not.'

My brother laughed. 'It's true!' he shouted. 'He puts his willie in her hole.'

'No, it's not and I'm going to sleep now.'

The next night was a Saturday. My sisters always went out together on Saturday nights – to The Royal in Tottenham. I watched them get ready as I always did and dreamed about the time I'd be going out somewhere. My brother went out too so I was left alone with my mum and dad and Saturday night television. My mum cooked fried bacon, beans and toast and she brought it to my dad and me on a tray. We ate it on our laps, my dad in his chair and me on

17

the floor in front of the fire. My mum didn't eat with us but sat down on the edge of the settee, poised to get up, ready to do something else. We watched *Dixon of Dock Green*. 'Evenin' all.' Then it was Val Doonican.

'Mum, you know what Johnny said?' I began.

There was no response. My mum stayed glued to Val as he rocked in his chair.

'You know what John said?' I went on.

My mum glanced fleetingly at me. She'd heard me.

'He said . . .' I began to get apprehensive over the disgusting thing I was about to say. But I had to clear it up. I had to be able to tell John for sure that he was completely wrong about reproduction. 'He said – that to make a baby, right . . .'

My mum's head turned to me and looked me in the eyes. My dad turned his head to me too.

'What?' she said impatiently.

'Nothing,' I said.

'What were you going to say, child?' my mum asked.

'Go on, Anne,' my dad said from his corner. I looked at my mum and then at my dad. I'd not had so much attention since the day my dad lifted me in the air and accidentally dropped me on my head.

I smiled. 'Oh nothing.'

'Go on,' my mum said, agitated. She looked over at my dad.

I was embarrassed. I laughed. 'He said . . .' I giggled. 'He said that the man . . .' I giggled some more. I wanted to run away.

'Go on, Angela – what did he tell you?' my mum insisted.

I took a deep breath. 'He said that the man has to stick his thing in the woman's hole.' I'd said it. I looked between them again and laughed.

'It's not true, is it? That's what he said.' I put my hand up to my mouth and forced more laughter. My mum and dad looked at one another wide-eyed and silent. Then my dad coughed and frowned. 'Who told you that? John?'

'Yeah – it's not true though, is it?' I asked again.

'When did he tell you that?' my dad said with a stern, straight face. My mum was looking at my dad and shaking her head slowly.

I stopped laughing. I wished I hadn't said anything – wished we could just go back to watching the telly in silence. I looked from my mum to my dad again.

'It's all right – 'cause it's not true – he just said it,' I said, trying to reassure them. 'He just made it up.'

My dad began to fidget on his seat. He was angry. 'When did he tell you this?'

'It's not true,' I said, anxious now not to get my brother into too much trouble.

My dad stood up and grabbed at his empty plate of food and left the room. I looked at my mum.

'Take no notice of what he said,' she said automatically. Then she got up and left me to Val Doonican and Paddy McGinty's goat.

When my brother came home, my mum and dad took him into their bedroom and shut the door, hard, behind them. I could hear muffled voices and after a few minutes the door opened. 'You hear me nuh,' my dad shouted.

'Yeah, yeah,' my brother said slowly as he went through the door of our bedroom.

My dad came into the living room looking flushed and muttering to himself. He saw me looking at him. 'You'll find out all these things soon enough, Anne,' he said shaking out his paper ferociously. I wasn't sure what he meant, but I smiled and nodded and looked back to the television.

I knew I'd got my brother into big trouble. Bigger than the time he forgot me and left me at the shops. Bigger even than the time he persuaded me to show my unusual protruding belly button to all his friends. I wished I hadn't said anything. I wished he hadn't told me anything. I was scared what my brother would do to me. Maybe he wouldn't speak to me any more. He stopped speaking to Patricia when she whacked him round the head after he'd chased her through the flat and wiped a bogey on her.

My brother was sitting in his bed reading when I went in. 'Why d'you tell them?' he said to me as I got ready for bed.

'I was only asking,' I said.

'Asking what?' he said.

'If it was true what you said.'

'You didn't have to ask them – I told you it was true!'

'Well it's not – Mum and Dad said it wasn't – so you shouldn't have said something like that,' I said, in the certainty that I had right on my side.

My brother rolled his eyes and turned his head away from my stare. 'I'm going to sleep now,' he said.

MY SISTERS

My sisters were bit of a mystery to me. They were teenagers, much older than me and they lived in a world of their own, which was in their bedroom. Their world stank of perfumes, hairsprays and creams you rubbed on to make yourself soft. The room was cluttered with clothes, jewellery, jars and make-up.

My sisters always had music playing in their room. They had an old record player, that sat on the floor. It had a stem and they would whack on layers of 45s. They'd drop down one by one and play Aretha Franklin, Ray Charles, Dionne Warwick, The Yardbirds, The Animals. There was a stack of LPs that leant up against the wall – Wilson Pickett, Lover Forever Changes, Johnny Winter,

Otis Redding. There was always music and smells in their room.

Yvonne was the eldest. My brother and me called her 'the batch' which was a polite way of saying 'the bitch'. She wore thick brown lines of make-up in the sockets of her eyes to give what she thought was that deep-set-eye look. In fact, it had the effect of making her look cruel. And to be fair, she *was* cruel. She didn't talk to anyone much except Patricia. She had no time for me except to ask for a favour.

'Angela, can you pass my bag?'

'No, get it yourself.'

'Go on.'

'No!'

'Go on – I'll let you try my jacket on.'

'No.'

'Oh, you little cow – I'll get it myself.'

She studied typing and shorthand after she left school at sixteen. She was a secretary and she earned a lot of money, which she spent on clothes, make-up, records and going out.

Patricia was a year younger than Yvonne but a foot taller. Patricia was a big girl. My brother and me called her 'the horse'. Her skin was much darker than anyone's in our family but her features were fine and more European. Sometimes she looked like she didn't belong to us. Sometimes I wished she didn't. Patricia was always miserable – she hardly ever smiled. She snarled and sulked. She'd buy a packet of sweets and sit humped over, eating her way through them.

'Can I have one?'

'No,' she'd say and twist her body away from me.

'Oh, go on, I gave you one yesterday.'

'No, get yer own.'

Patricia and my brother stopped speaking to each other when she was twelve. You had to talk through them.

21

'John, Patricia says that Mum said not to forget to get some extra milk.'

'Tell her I got it – and that she can get stuffed.'

Before they stopped talking over the incident with the bogey they had always done things together. But since then, Patricia and Yvonne had become like twins.

Every Saturday night they went out – to a club or to see a group. They went to see The Yardbirds 'live' at a club. This was a special occasion. Yvonne loved The Yardbirds. She had their picture on her wall along with a lot of other groups.

'Which one are you goin' to see?' I asked.

'There,' she said, pointing to a picture of a group of blond-haired men standing around in a field.

'Which one's your favourite?' I asked.

'Oh shu' up,' she said. 'I don't have favourites – I'm not a kid.'

My sisters started getting ready for this special occasion early on Saturday afternoon. They let me watch on the understanding that I didn't say a 'bleedin' word'. They began with baths and white face packs. Then they rolled their hair into heated hair rollers. And all the time they talked about boys.

'I'm not sure I fancy him.'

'He's all right. Better than Jimmy – he'd be nice if it wasn't for his hair.'

'Yeah, and his teeth.'

'Yeah – there's his teeth I suppose – still, they're better than Jimmy's.'

'Yeah, but I don't like that jacket he wears.'

'I know. That's awful – someone should tell him.'

'They have for a joke – he says he likes it.'

''Struth really – well, Jimmy's not that bad.'

Yvonne had a lot of boyfriends. Sometimes one would call to take her out and he'd sit embarrassed in the front room while the rest of the family sat staring and smiling around him. When they had gone my dad would always say he didn't like the look of him and my mum would say, 'Seemed nice enough.'

Patricia had one boy call for her once. But my brother and me made so much fun of his squinting eye that she had never dared to try another one out on us – although I heard her talk about them.

Yvonne had bought a new yellow two-piece suit from Biba which she was going to wear. Patricia was still at school in the sixth form. She didn't have money to spend on clothes and none of Yvonne's things fitted her. But she still managed with her brown mini-skirt with the wide leather belt and a skinny rib cut-away-sleeved jumper.

They put on thick black eyeliner and false eyelashes that they stuck on with glue from a small tube. They painted their nails and blew on them to get them dry. Yvonne put on her false bit, a piece of hair that she attached to her own hair to give the impression of a long pony tail. The false bit was made from real hair. Real dead straight hair. My sister pulled her fuzzy hair back tight on her head, then attached the long waist-length unknown person's hair to it and concealed the join with a band.

'It looks so plain, just like a drink of water – what's the matter with your own hair?' my mum said. But my mum was dismissed as old-fashioned.

'More like a horse's arse than a pony's tail,' my brother laughed.

Patricia had different hair to Yvonne. Thicker and straighter. She'd had it cut into a bob with a fringe which hung down over one eye but not the other. People said she looked like a model.

They put on white lipstick and spent a long time in front of the long mirror vying for space and adjusting their clothes. I thought they looked wonderful. When they were ready they came in to the front room to get their instructions from my dad.

'Cha – you going out with your clothes only half on?' my dad said.

'Dad, it's the fashion.'

'You'll catch a cold – put something on yer legs nuh.'

'Dad!' my sisters said together.

My dad tutted, defeated. 'See yer back before eleven.'

'Not eleven, Dad. It doesn't finish till eleven – twelve, we'll be back by twelve.'

'Half past eleven then,' my dad said and went back to the television.

''Struth,' Patricia muttered to herself. She looked at Yvonne, rolled her eyes, then they both left.

My sisters made such a commotion when they came home later that I got out of bed.

'I couldn't believe it, Mum – I just couldn't believe it.' Yvonne was leaning against the wall looking like a small band of angels was buzzing round in front of her eyes. She saw me and looked pleased. Something had happened.

'Oh, Angela – you'll never guess what happened – it was great.' She made movements like her legs were giving way underneath her – like she was going to faint. Patricia stood beside her, unexcited.

'What?' I asked.

'You know the singer of the group?'

'What group?'

'The Yardbirds!' she shouted. 'You know the singer – well . . .'

'Which one's the singer?' I asked.

'Oh just listen!' she said, irritated. 'The singer, the singer!' she shouted.

'Sschh, child – you want everybody to hear?' my mum said.

'Well . . .' she said more quietly, back in her dreamy state.

24

'He spoke to her,' Patricia said without emotion.

'He didn't *only* speak to me,' Yvonne corrected. 'He didn't *only* speak to me,' she repeated, looking at me.

'What?' I asked.

'Oh, he's so gorgeous,' she said, looking to the ceiling. My mum left and went to her room.

'What?' I asked again.

'Well, he came up to me and asked me to dance.'

'Really!' I said.

'I know, I couldn't believe it . . . but in the interval bit he asked me to dance. I nearly fainted. On my life I nearly fainted. He said he'd seen me when he was playing. I nearly fainted – honest. I went all weak,' she began to giggle. Patricia rolled her eyes.

'Did you dance with him then?'

'Of course – God, he's so lovely – his hair is so lovely. I just wanted to touch it.'

'Did you?'

'No, but listen – that's not all that happened. He had to go back on stage, you know, and play again. Oh, Angela, he's so gorgeous I couldn't believe it. Then he's singing right, and he starts waving to someone. Well, I looks behind me then Pat says he's waving at me. And he was! I nearly passed out. Pat just rolled up. I was so surprised. I just couldn't believe it. He was singing and waving at me. So I waved back and these girls started saying, 'Who's he waving at?' and they saw me. They went green – they were so jealous.'

'Then what happened?' I asked eagerly.

Yvonne's face dropped and she stood up straight. 'Then we had to bloody come home thanks to . . .' she nodded her head towards my mum and dad's bedroom.

'Will you see him again?'

'Doubt it – but I felt so good – I mean, out of all the girls there he could have picked . . . he could have picked anyone . . . I mean out of all the girls . . . I was walking on air, I tell ya. I was walking on air.'

'I'm going to bed,' Patricia said.

Just then my dad came out of his bedroom. 'What's all this noise you making? And what sort of time you call this to come home?' he said, raising his voice in a whisper. 'Get to bed now you hear.'

Yvonne tutted loud and long.

'And don't give me any of yer cheek. Comin' home in the middle of the night with yer noise.'

'It's not the middle of the night – we're not late,' Yvonne snarled.

My dad looked dumbfounded. 'Don't talk to me like that, child, or you know what you'll get,' he shouted.

'Oh shu' up!' my sister said quietly as she walked to her room.

'What did you say – I hear that. What did you . . .' He started grappling on the back of his bedroom door for something, then he pulled out his brown leather belt. 'Come here – I'll give you cheek,' he said, flicking the belt at my sister.

Yvonne ran for her door and closed it behind her. 'You spoil everything,' she shouted in a tearful voice. 'I hate you.'

My dad pushed at the door but he couldn't open it. 'I'll see you tomorrow – you hear?' he threatened through the door. Then he looked at me. 'What you doing up – who said you could get up – get back to bed.'

THE CAT

'I don't want a cat – I don't like them – they mess up the place,' my mum said.

'But Mum, cats are clean – they're always washing and that,' I said.

'It still has to toilet and who clears it up?'

'I will,' I said.

'You will!' my mum repeated with disbelief in her voice. 'You will. I've heard that before. What about when you get fed up . . . ?'

'I won't get fed up.'

'Who's going to feed it when you get fed up?' she went on, oblivious to my last comment.

'I'll feed it – honest. I'll do *everything*.'

My mum looked at me. 'Yes, and you said that about the budgie and the hamster.'

'I *did* look after the hamster,' I shouted.

'Well – what about the poor budgie? Your dad had to feed it and clean it out.'

'That's different,' I said.

'How's it different? You children couldn't even remember what the poor bird was called.'

I tried not to smile at the thought of the budgie, but it was difficult. We had the budgie for years – it sat in its cage chirping, looking in the mirror, sharpening its beak on the bits of cuttlefish and shitting. One day we heard a thud and looked in the budgie's cage and it was lying stiff on the bottom – its little legs in the air. My brother took it out and we all felt it. It felt like it was made of cardboard. We tried to look sad but then John said, 'Can anyone remember its name?' and we all started to laugh. Poor budgie.

'It just plop in the cage and nobody care,' my mum went on. 'You just laughed.'

'I never laughed – it was the others – the others that laughed – I never.'

'Well – you get fed up with the animals, then it's your dad and me that has all the trouble.'

'I'll take care of it – I promise – I'll cross my heart – look – look.' My mum didn't look at me crossing my heart, she just carried on stirring the pan on the cooker.

'I don't like cats,' she said.

'You said that about hamsters but you liked it when I brought it home.'

'That's different.'

'How?' I asked.

'It's just different.'

'Why – why's it different?'

'It just is.'

'Why – just tell me why?'

'Oh, child, stop with your nagging!' There was silence. 'What your dad say?' my mum asked quietly.

'He said I'm to ask you.'

There was another silence.

'You promise you'll clean up all its mess?' she said.

'Yes – honest – I swear – I promise – cross my heart.'

'All right, but . . .' I didn't hear what else she said.

'Thanks Mum, thanks Mum!' I yelled, jumping up on her.

'Calm down – calm down. You hear me, you hear what I said? You mind you take care of it and don't bring it near me. I don't like cats,' she said.

I nodded furiously. 'Can I have eight and six then, Mum?'

'What for?' she said, frowning at me.

'To buy the cat!'

'Cha,' my mum said, and sighed.

'Oh, she's so sweet – look at her – so sweet.' My mum knelt down on the floor, to be at kitten height. 'She's so pretty – let me hold her,' and she lifted the cat gently. 'So small – you feel you'll crush her,' she said looking at me, 'but I just *must* get a kiss of this little head.' She kissed the top of the kitten's head.

'I told you you'd like her,' I said.

'So sweet – you're a little sweet thing – ahh, look at her.' My mum was in a world of her own.

'We're going to call her Wilhelmina,' I said. 'Pat thought

28

of it – she said there's some model called that – Wilhelmina. Or Willie for short.'

'Ahh, Willie – little Willie – is your name little Willie?' my mum carried on in a high-pitched squeaky voice.

Willie became part of our family, as much as any human. But somewhere we went wrong in her upbringing. She could be a soppy, doting cat who would put her front paws up on your leg. When you picked her up she'd cling round your neck, like a baby, purring and occasionally licking at your face. She'd lie in front of the fire, stretched out long, purring in her sleep. *But,* if you tried to pick her up for a cuddle and she didn't want you to, she would turn on you, spitting and snarling and lashing out with open claws. And sometimes you could stroke her as she lay on her back and she'd purr and roll this way and that. And sometimes she'd grab your hand and sink her teeth in and push away with her back legs.

One of her favourite sports was to sit under the settee – then, as someone walked past, she would pounce out on them, grab them round the ankle, bite them and run off and hide until someone else walked by. Sometimes she'd cling to your ankle and you'd have to shake her off and scream at her to leave you alone.

She was a fussy eater and only ate pigs' kidneys or special tuna cat food. If you gave her anything else it just sat in her bowl, because she would rather starve than eat it.

Willie sat on the window sill, in the front room, most of the day and looked out or climbed out of the six-inch gap left open for her. But she also learned to knock at the front door and when you opened it to her she came in whimpering – moaning to herself that it wasn't opened sooner.

THE TELLY

Sundays were lazy days in our family. At least for me and

my dad. My sisters always seemed to be with friends or boyfriends and my brother was always out somewhere unspecified – 'Anywhere,' he would say. My mum spent most of Sunday, after church, in the kitchen. She'd only come out briefly when we would see her staring at the television through the crack left by the open door.

'Come and sit down, Mum,' I'd say.

'No, I'm just waiting for something to boil,' she'd say and then she would silently vanish after a short while.

My dad got up late, had a wash, got dressed and then lay down again, this time on the settee in our front room.

Our front room was packed with furniture. Every bit of wall space had something pressed against it. There was a green three-piece suite with a long settee that could double up as a bed should we have any guests – which we never did. A bookcase with volumes of the *Encyclopaedia Britannica* placed untouched, practically where the extremely convincing salesman had left them.

There was also a dining-table with a flap that could be put up, if we ever felt like eating at it – but we never did. This dark brown wooden table had a long curved scratch all the way down it which had never been removed. My mum liked to keep it to remind my brother of the night he came home reeling drunk from his Christmas party at work. He was pushed through the door by his workmates. He was singing, 'Cold turkey has got me . . .' He then fell over a chair which gouged the offending mark down the table. Then he was sick on the carpet. Luckily my mum felt the scratch was enough to remind him of his waywardness and the sick was cleared up.

There was a radiogram against another wall. A brown, wooden, polished box with a cloth front and fake gold knobs. In the side cabinet was the turntable with a stem ready and waiting for your 45s.

The fireplace was made from mottled, pale brown tiles and in it sat a large electric fire. Then there was the television. The television was the focal point of the room. All objects and furniture seemed to tilt towards it. It was the first thing you saw when you came in and no matter where you sat you would always have a very good view of it.

The television was on nearly all day on Sunday. My dad began his viewing with football, *The Big Match.* I sat on the floor by the fire and did my homework with my dad lying behind me on the settee, occasionally pushing my head to one side if it got in the way of his view.

'Sit up then,' I'd say. 'You'd see better.'

'Cha, nuh man,' he'd reply, pushing my head a little more. He supported Arsenal. He felt he should as we lived next to the stadium. But any goal from any team would make him shout, 'Yes!'

After *The Big Match* we watched *The Golden Shot.* 'Bernie the Bolt,' we said in unison, at the appropriate time. My brother said *The Golden Shot* was the reason he left home at the age of fifteen to hitchhike round Europe. He just couldn't stand to watch another one.

My dad never shared his Sunday settee. If anyone asked if they could sit on it he would create a small triangle of space in front of his stomach, pat it and say, 'Sit here nuh man.' Nobody ever did sit in this space although I did try once but my dad just kept moaning that I was crushing him.

When all the good Sunday programmes finished and it became what my dad called 'God bother hour', he got up and fetched the ironing board. On every Sunday night for as long as I can remember at about half past six my dad would go and get the ironing board. The board had a green plastic seat attached to it so my dad could sit while ironing and it was lovingly covered in a new cloth every two months. When the board was in place (so that he had a good view of the television) and an ashtray positioned at arm's length, my dad got the wash basket.

31

My mum spent most of her 'leisure' hours washing for her family, all by hand. By the end of the week there was quite a pile in the basket. And my dad ironed everything – shirts, skirts, sheets, towels, handkerchiefs, knickers, gloves. If it was in the basket it got ironed unless somebody stopped him. 'No Dad, not that, it's rubber! No Dad, that's a pencil!'

When he was finished there would be several neat piles – large items on the bottom getting smaller to the top. My dad was an expert ironer. My teacher at school once said, 'Angela, who ironed your dress – it's wonderful.' She laughed when I said it was my dad – so did my school friends. 'Dads don't do ironing,' my friend confided to me later.

We watched a lot of television in our family. From the moment I got home from school the television was on. I viewed with my sisters and brother during the week, switching channels when something 'boring' came on to find something more interesting, even if only marginally more interesting. My mum never really watched anything. After she made dinner she sat in her room studying for an Open University degree. She used to watch her course programmes but they were always early in the morning before I got up or else late at night after I'd gone to bed.

At about nine o'clock my dad got home from work. Every weekday evening it was the same. We all sat watching the telly as my dad poked his head around the living-room door and said, 'D'evenin'.' Never 'good evening' from which 'd'evenin' had distilled, or even 'Hi kids, Daddy's home.' It was always, 'D'evenin'.' Usually no one would take any notice. Occasionally I might look towards the door where the 'D'evenin'' came from but I wouldn't make a verbal reply. The only time there was ever any enthusiastic response was if my dad was carrying a brown paper bag. Then one of us would usually say, 'What's in the bag?' and someone else would insist that they should see it first. This was because it might have contained chocolate biscuits given to my dad by 'a lady he knows'.

My dad then said, 'Where's Mum?' and left the doorway without waiting for an answer. Or he'd chastize us with, 'Every light in the house burnin',' if he saw a light on in a room that nobody was in.

If my mum was sitting in the living room with us, watching something of interest to her – a nature programme perhaps – my dad would walk over to her and give her a kiss on the cheek. No, kiss is not quite the right word. My parents didn't really kiss each other – they sort of sniffed at one another. My dad would put his face close to my mum's cheek and my mum would lean her cheek over towards him but twist her lips the other way so there was no chance that the kiss would get her on the mouth. As they touched they'd both take a sharp inhalation of breath through the nose and that was it.

After finding my mum he'd remove his coat and jacket and hang them in the wardrobe, brushing any dirt or hairs off. 'What you watching?' he'd say as he came back into the room, to which he would get no reply. Then, as sure as night follows day, he'd walk to the television set and begin to fiddle with the knobs.

'Oh, Dad!' we'd all say together. 'It was all right till you started fiddling with it.'

'I'm just looking,' my dad would say, appealing for calm. Or 'It looked a bit dark to me' or 'It's flickering a bit' or 'It's a bit loud.' Then he'd position himself in front of the telly so our only view was of his grey-trousered backside with a white hanky hanging out of his back pocket. Most of my childhood was spent looking at the two grey cheeks of my dad's backside as he fiddled with the telly. It was useless to protest. Once he'd started, he'd have to get it right.

'It's fine now, Dad,' we'd shout every few minutes but

our opinion was not valued – my dad had to satisfy himself.

My dad would often spend whole weekends fiddling with the television. He would take the back off, remove valves, tinker with wires, take bits out and hold them up to the light. When we protested that we'd like to watch something, he'd look at us incredulously and say, 'That's why people don't like to have children.' When the TV repair man finally had to be called my dad would swear, with an innocent face, that he never touched the telly and no, no, no, he never had the back off.

Sometimes he would come in and simply turn the TV over. 'Daaaad!' we'd all scream, to which he would reply, 'Watch this nuh man it's good.' This usually happened when there was a midweek football or boxing match. If we protested any more, which we did depending on the quality of the programme (for example, *Ready, Steady, Go* would get a full fifteen minutes of moaning from my sisters, whereas the Wednesday play would only get a disgruntled thirty seconds), my dad would say, 'Cha – I don't get to see much television – you watch it all night – it's only fair.'

Chapter 2

It was two days before my dad retired that he began to limp. I sent him a card. 'Good luck in your retirement' it said.

'What are you going to do?' I asked him.

'I don't know – this and that,' he said.

He had no immediate plans. Then his right leg became weak and he walked dragging it. He then found that he could not use his right hand properly. He would go to pick up something but find his grip was not sufficient to lift it.

I could tell that my dad was worried by what was happening to his body. He made an appointment to see his GP and he began to 'take care of himself'. He would pour himself a pint of full-cream milk once, sometimes twice a day, and drink it all.

'You shouldn't drink so much milk,' I said to him.

'Got to keep up me strength,' he replied.

'But it's not good for you, Dad – too much fat.'

He looked at me, bewildered. 'What – milk not good for you any more – since when?'

My dad had never really been seriously ill. But he would go to the doctor with just a cold and then come back complaining that he was not prescribed anything. He never accepted that there was no cure for the common cold; he was convinced they were keeping it from him alone.

When he had a cold he would lie in bed moaning and whimpering like a feeble dog. My mum would fetch and

35

carry and roll her eyes when we asked how he was. But he was behaving differently with his new complaints. He became stoical. He said it was 'nothing'. Then he dragged his leg into the garden and pruned the mallow tree to a stump with a hand that barely functioned. He tried to show us that he could do what he had always done – except that he had never done it before.

He came back from the doctor looking smaller and greyer. For once the doctor did not shrug him off. He did not tell my dad that he was imagining things, that there was nothing really wrong with him, that he should go home and calm down. For once the doctor took him seriously and made an appointment for him to see a specialist at the hospital.

The specialist told my dad that he should come into hospital for 'tests'. He went back the next day and was admitted into the men's ward.

Most of the ward was split into small rooms with four beds in each. All the other beds were taken but their occupants roamed around the ward and corridors – none of them sick enough to just stay put. My dad was no exception. He greeted me at the lift, dressed in a dressing-gown that he'd had for twenty years – thick brushed wool in dark red, with red and beige piping and belt. It fitted him better than it had a few years ago – he'd shrunk to fit it. Underneath he wore striped winceyette pyjamas which he kept adjusting so the fly hole did not reveal anything it shouldn't.

As I walked through the ward with him he waved and smiled at people we passed – nurses, patients, orderlies. He turned and said, 'All right, mate?' raising a thumb in the air to a man lying on a bed who smiled and waved back.

'See that man?' he said, nodding his head in the direction of a young man who was deep in conversation with his visitor. 'He's just come out of intensive care. You know why?' he said, leaning closer towards me. I shook my head and tried not to stare too obviously.

'Eating fish,' he said slowly.

'Fish?' I repeated, still staring at the man.

'Yes – eating bad fish. On holiday, not here in this country,' he went on. 'He just pass out at the airport and they brought him here to intensive care – from fish.'

We both stared for some moments longer then I looked around the small room.

'What about him?' I whispered, nodding toward a frail-looking man with long black dreadlocks who had just laid down on a bed.

'Oh,' my dad whispered, 'a diabetic.' We both stared silently at the man.

'So,' I said after a pause, clapping my hands, 'how are you? What have the doctors said?' I didn't want to ask but I was sure that I could have sat with him all day and he would not have brought the subject up himself. He sat back on the bed and adjusted his pyjamas again.

'Oh, it's nothing much,' he said with a wave of his hand. 'Just a mild stroke they say – that's why me hand and leg gone a bit funny.' He then held his right hand in his left like it was an injured bird. 'Just a mild stroke,' he repeated.

'Well, that would make sense,' I said cheerfully. 'So what are they going to do?'

'Someone's coming to help me do exercises – get back me strength.'

'A physiotherapist?' I said.

My dad looked at me. 'What's it called?' he asked.

'A physiotherapist.'

'Something like that – yes, something like that,' he muttered looking at the ceiling. 'There's a bloke in another room had a stroke – worse than mine. He has that thing too. They come and make you lift your leg and that.'

He was content. The fear that had invaded his features at home had gone. Putting a name to his condition had satisfied him. Stroke was an acceptable name to my dad. I caught his mood.

'So when are you coming out?' I chirped.

'Oh soon, soon – they're doing another test tomorrow.'

'What's that for?'

'Something about a shadow on me lung which cause something to happen in me head.'

I tried not to look alarmed.

'What are they going to do to your head?' I asked.

'Just some X-ray – can't eat before. They just want to make sure or something.'

'A brain scan,' I said, a little too surprised.

'Don't know,' he replied, looking agitated. 'It's just to see.'

'To see what?'

'Just to see if that's what cause the shadow – just to see.' The words seemed to have no relevance to him – they were repeated but seemingly not understood. I didn't understand either but I knew I couldn't ask for any more information from my dad. But I asked myself, 'What does a shadow on a lung have to do with a stroke?'

'Did you speak to the doctors?' I asked.

'Yer mum saw them,' he said. 'She told me that they'd said I'd had a mild stroke.'

'They didn't talk to you?'

'No, yer mum talked to them,' he said. He began to look through the drawer of his bedside table. It was time to change the subject.

'Oh Dad, I've brought you some food,' I said, unpacking a carrier bag.

Chapter 3

THE DREAM

Our main family outing every year was to the Ideal Home Exhibition. Before we started having regular holidays at Pontin's, the Ideal Home Exhibition was considered such a treat that it made up for the fact that we hadn't left home.

We went on the tube. It was fine all the way to Earl's Court on the Piccadilly line, but then we had to change. Then we hit the crowds. Masses of families migrating, packing on to trains. Being herded by megaphone announcements round this corner, up this tunnel, through this gate – until you could see the booking hall in sight. Bright lights up ahead waiting. But first a long slow, shuffling queue for tickets, which seemed to take for ever. When we finally got into the hall the journey and the transformation – from stark grey exterior to multi-colours, music, the smell of food and bustling people now going this way and that at will – was like having arrived in a different country.

I held on tight to my dad. I knew that if I got lost in the crowd they would never find me again.

Six individuals all wanted to see different things, have different experiences. I was very fond of the bendy toys. A stall of all your favourite cartoon characters made of rubber and wire so you could bend their legs, arms, head and body into all sorts of poses. I stood silently by the stall every year, being as good as I could, bending the sample Bugs Bunny and not nagging in the hope that my dad would see my wanting and hand over the necessary cash. He never did. I just got pulled away after a few minutes' indulgence. I waved goodbye to Bugs and Bugs waved back.

My sisters liked to spend their time around the tights and stockings stall. They looked through endless packets and pointed at the dismembered legs that showed you how your legs could look if only you bought the tights. Saturday jobs meant that they were more participants on their stall than I was. But they had to choose carefully. We were there a long time.

My brother liked models and kits. My mum liked the demonstration of pressure cookers. There was a little area like a small theatre where we all sat in rows. Then a man came and demonstrated how easy and quick it was to cook using this new method. He produced a whole meal in front of our eyes in a few minutes. 'And now for the gravy,' he said. He then swilled some water around in the bottom of the pressure cooker. Within seconds he poured out a brown liquid that was, for sure, tasty gravy. My mum gasped.

'Are you going to get one, Mum?'

My mum looked at my dad, who quickly looked off into the distance, or tied his shoe lace or took out a cigarette.

'Next year, maybe,' she said.

After the demonstration was over you could go up and taste the food. My brother and I ran to the front and were shooed away by the man. He did it so only we could see. Only we knew we were to get lost. Then he beckoned the monied adults up to have a taste. My mum went forward and smelt the gravy. 'Very nice, very nice,' she said.

'Can I give you a leaflet, madam?' the man asked.

My mum stared at the pictures. 'Very nice,' she nodded.

There was a whole floor that my dad liked – well, we all

did but this was my dad's place. It was full of gadgets. Things to 'help' you round the house. Stall after stall: a slicer that cuts cucumber into long spirals; a window wiper that can clean both sides of the window at once; a sponge mop that 'drinks' spills and leaves your carpet unstained; a sticky brush for removing dirt and unsightly hairs from your clothes; a bag that's six bags in one; an ironing-board cover with a revolutionary coating. All had special qualities and all fascinated my dad.

We moved from stall to stall saying, 'That's great! . . . Oh, that would be handy! . . . Oohh, that's good! . . . Ooh, that's just what I need!' My dad jangled loose change around in his trouser pocket and bought nothing.

But the place we all liked the best, the place we all agreed was the best, the reason we came, were the houses.

It was called 'the village' because there were actual houses built there. Seven or eight with gardens and fountains. We queued up, then when our turn came we edged through the house looking at each room.

'This would be my bedroom, Dad – look at that bendy toy on the bed.'

We marvelled at bathrooms and sitting rooms, conservatories, bedrooms and studies, granny flats and garages. Each house was different and when we finished in one we queued up to see around another. And on the way home we argued about which house to get.

'The first was lovely,' my mum said. 'It had a lovely desk and light – I'd like that.'

'No, no, not that one Mum. It had no stairs.'

'I know. That's what I liked too.'

'No, no, we've got to have stairs!'

Then we went into our flats. Red brick with long open balconies built round a grey, concreted yard. Built in the thirties to house the poor. If we owned them all, I imagined, it would be a mansion. We went inside our little council home, choked full of furniture – bulging with items for a family of six. In need of decoration, in need of being ten times the size, in need of a staircase. And the row started again.

'No, I think we should get that nice bungalow,' my mum insisted.

I got agitated. 'Not the bungalow – not the bungalow. Dad, you don't want to get the bungalow, do you – you want somewhere with stairs too – don't you, Dad?'

My dad looked at me. 'Calm down, Anne – we're not getting any of the houses really.'

'What do you mean!' I said, shocked.

'We can't afford those houses, Anne – it's just talk.'

THE FRIEND

'What is it?' Sonia said, turning up a corner of her mouth and pushing her fork through the rice on the plate.

'Eat it – go on, try it – you'll like it. It's nice, isn't it, Angela?' my mum said, turning to me. My friend Sonia had come for her tea. I watched her prod at the brown, stewed meat.

'My mum says I shouldn't eat things like this,' she said.

'How yer mum know what yer eating?' my mum asked with rising impatience.

'She says I don't have to eat anything I don't like and I don't like this.'

'You haven't tried it, child – how you know you don't like it?'

Sonia stared sullenly at her plate.

My mum tutted and rolled her eyes, then left the room.

'It's nice, Sonia. Go on, try it – try it – it's just meat. Look.' I took a mouthful of the stew. We had this a lot at home. A spiced stew with rice and peas.

'What are these bits?' she asked, pointing to the kidney beans in the rice.

'They're beans – like baked beans, only they're red.'

'They don't look like baked beans.'

'They're not baked beans, but they're beans like baked beans are.'

'Well, I don't like them,' she stated, spearing one with her fork then wiping it off on to the side of her plate. Sonia put a piece of the meat to her mouth and nibbled off some of the sauce with her lips.

'Urghh, it's burning my mouth.' She dropped her fork back on to the plate and grabbed for her glass of orange squash. 'I don't like it,' she said, breathless after taking a gulp of the squash. 'My mum says I don't have to eat anything I don't like.' She coughed and held her chest like she was trying to expel something from her throat.

'I don't feel well now. My mum says I'm not to eat things like this because I've got a bad chest and ear.' She pushed her plate away from her. 'I'd better go home,' she said, looking away from me.

'You've only just come,' I pleaded.

'Yeah, but I don't feel well. My mum said I should go home if I don't feel well.'

'Oh don't go – don't go yet – there's cake for afters.'

Sonia looked at me, interested. 'Cake – from a shop?' she asked.

I didn't answer. I didn't want to tell her my mum baked it, but my silence did and her face dropped back to its sullenness.

'No, I think I'd better go home now – I don't feel well.'

She jumped from her chair and ran through the flat to the front door. I held the door open after her and watched her walk quickly down the balcony.

'Are you coming out to play later?' I called after her but she didn't answer.

My mum put her head out of the kitchen. 'She gone?' she said, surprised.

'She didn't feel well,' I said.

43

'Stupid girl,' my mum said loudly. 'You finish the food?'

'Sonia left hers,' I said.

'Cha – stupid girl,' my mum muttered, shaking her head. We went into the front room to the abandoned plates.

'Look at this – the child waste all the food,' my mum said. 'Come – you eat up now.'

I sat down and put some stew and rice in my mouth but my appetite had gone. I looked at my mum and wished she'd fried up sausages and chips with Oxo gravy poured over the top like Sonia had at her home. Or that my mum's cooking was more like school dinners.

I loved school dinners. I looked forward to them every day. My friends didn't. They all screwed up their faces and said, 'Ehh!' a lot and that their mums cooked better things. Nicer. But my mum didn't. She couldn't cook steak and kidney pie with a rich crusty pastry that melted in your mouth. That was cut into squares from a large metal tin and if you were lucky you'd get the corner bit with more pastry and less meat. Then you'd have two ice-cream-scoop spoonfuls of mashed potato. With lumps or without, it was delicious mashed with the pie crust, peas and gravy. And there were chips, beans and fried spam fritters that left your lips glossy with grease. Slices of brown roast meat – what animal it came from you could never tell – but you had it with roast potatoes glistening brown and occasionally crispy. And brown gravy that floated over the top and mingled with your boiled carrots.

And the puddings. Like no puddings we ever got at home. Caramel tart all golden and gooey – nobody was sure what it was made of but it tasted sweet and melted in the hot custard, forming lines and brown swirls in the yellow. Or chocolate sponge pudding with chocolate custard to match. Or semolina with a drop of rosehip syrup, sitting pretty in the middle.

But *my* mum cooked different things. She boiled rice in coconut with beans. She spiced chicken and meat until it was hot. She fried bananas. Everything she made tasted different.

My mum watched me take some more mouthfuls as she took small forkfuls of meat from Sonia's abandoned plate.

'I can't eat any more,' I said. My mum looked at my plate.

'Cha you're just as bad as that stupid child – eat up the good food.'

'I can't,' I insisted.

My mum grabbed the two plates from the table in a grumpy silence and left the room.

I went up to Sonia's flat to see if she could come out. We were meant to have tea at my house then go out and play around the yard on the swings. She lived on the third-floor balcony of the flats – I lived on the ground floor. Her flat was almost the same as ours but it smelt differently.

Sonia's mum answered the door. 'Hello chuck,' she said. Sonia's mum came from somewhere 'up north'. I wasn't sure where but Sonia went for her holidays to Blackpool and she'd say how much nicer it was 'up north' – how the people were much friendlier and how they'd like to live there again one day. Sonia's mum was a dinner lady at school. At lunchtimes she'd wink at me and give me extra portions if I wanted it because I was Sonia's friend.

'Is Sonia in?' I asked.

'Come in, come in,' she sang. 'She's sitting by the fire – she's just had a bath.'

Sonia was an only child. She had a bedroom of her own and a mum all to herself. She didn't have a dad. He died or was killed or something. There was a photo of him that sat on the mantelpiece but Sonia was very hazy about how he actually died.

I smiled at Sonia, who was sitting on the floor fluffing at her straight hair with a towel. She smiled at me but didn't say anything. I sat on the settee.

'Are you coming out?' I asked.

'Me hair's wet – Mum won't let me with wet hair,' she answered.

Her mum came in and sat close beside me on the settee. 'So,' she said, looking at me and grinning. 'Sonia told me what she had to eat at your house.'

It was very hot in the room. I smiled. Sonia's mum laughed then said, 'She said it was so hot it nearly blew her head off.' She laughed and so did Sonia.

'It *was*, Mum!' Sonia said from the floor. 'My head nearly went pooom.' Sonia made the noise of a small bomb exploding and waved her arms in the air, and they laughed. I smiled.

'Is that what you eat all the time?' Sonia's mum asked me.

'Not all the time,' I said.

'What else d'you eat then?' she persisted.

'Other things,' I said.

'Like what?'

I thought. 'Sausages and that.'

'Ordinary sausages, or special jungle sausages?' She laughed and put her arm around my shoulders and gave me a squeeze. 'I'm only joking – only teasing,' she said. 'No – what else do you eat?'

'I can't remember,' I said.

'Can't remember what you eat – that's daft! Sonia can remember what she eats, can't you chuck?'

Sonia nodded. 'I eat normal food,' she said.

'So do we,' I said. 'Most of the time.'

'Sonia says your mum fries bananas and you eat them with potatoes – is that true?'

'Well, they're like bananas,' I said tentatively.

'It's true then!' she said, surprised. 'I thought she was

46

making it up.' She laughed again. 'We like bananas with custard.'

'So do I,' I said. Sonia's mum looked at me and gave me another squeeze.

'Ooh, you are funny, Angela,' she said, grinning. 'Don't suppose you like all that hot food then?' she went on.

'Not really,' I said.

'I didn't think so – little girls like you shouldn't eat hot things. It made Sonia feel poorly.' I nodded.

'Are you coming out, Sonia?' I said to my friend.

'She can't come out, chuck – her hair's wet. You can stay in and play if you like. I'll fry you both some bananas,' she said with a straight face.

'Ooh don't, mum,' Sonia said anxiously.

'I'm only teasing,' she laughed. 'Are you stopping then, Angela?'

'No,' I said. 'I have to go now.'

THE MEATBALLS

My mum went away to an Open University summer school. She gave us good warning that she would be going. I'd known for about a year. But it still seemed to come as a bit of a shock to my dad.

'Oh, you going so soon?' he asked.

'I told you from a long time, Dad,' my mum protested.

'Yes, but I didn't realize it was so soon.'

My mum gave instructions for most household chores and appointed someone to each task.

'And Dad,' she said, 'I've left some meatballs in the kitchen. They just need frying up to heat them through – they should be all right.'

At tea time an acrid smell began to envelop the flat. I went into the kitchen. My dad was standing over the stove, as smoke wafted up all around him. I'd never seen him cook before. He was pushing at something in a frying pan, jabbing it like he was trying to kill it over again.

'What's that smell, Dad?' I asked.

'Meatballs,' he said.

He looked intently at the pan. There were three plates to the side of the cooker. Each one had three boiled potatoes and a small pile of peas on it.

'What's for tea, Dad?' I said, hoping it was something else.

'Meatballs,' he said.

'They smell a bit funny Dad,' I said.

'Cha,' he said, turning and scowling at me. 'Get out from under my feet.' So I left the kitchen.

'What's that smell?' my brother asked.

'Meatballs,' I repeated.

'They pong,' he said. I shrugged.

My dad came in from the kitchen and lifted up the flap in the table. We never ate at this table when my mum was around. We always ate balancing the plates on our lap and watching the television. But there was only my dad, my brother and me and the difference meant that everything changed. My dad threw down a bundle of cutlery on to the table.

'Come Angela, put on the knives and forks.'

I laid them out as best I could on the tiny table – it was hard to fit three sets on and have enough room for you to move your arms.

My dad came in again carrying a bowl filled with tinned peaches. He set them down in the middle of the table and smiled at me. 'They're for afters, if you eat everything up.'

I looked at my brother and we rolled our eyes. Then my dad came in with the three plates. The meatballs were steaming hot and with the steam came an awful stench of rotting flesh.

'Dad, those meatballs don't smell right,' I said. My

brother stuck his nose over his and pulled a face. We sat at the table.

'Come – eat up,' my dad said.

I looked at my brother then cut into the now-cold potatoes. My brother's mouth was still curled up at the edges.

'Come – eat!' my dad insisted. As he did a pea shot out from his mouth and landed in the bowl of tinned peaches. I watched it shoot out and land with an audible plop right in the centre of the bowl. My dad looked at the pea, quickly removed it and put it back in his mouth. Then he cut into one of his meatballs and the smell wafted up to him. 'Oh dear,' he said. 'I don't think these are right.'

'I feel sick,' my brother said, pushing his plate away.

'Well, just eat up your peas and potato nuh.'

My brother and I sat back from the table and folded our arms.

'Cha,' my dad said. He grabbed our plates and scraped the meatballs on to the copy of the *Daily Mirror*. Then he scraped his own off.

'I'll give them to the dogs,' he said.

We followed him to the front door. He opened it and tossed the meatballs out on to the grey concrete of the yard that the flats were built around. He turned back to us screwing up the paper. 'The dogs can have them. Now eat up the rest or you won't get any peaches.'

The next morning my friend knocked at the door. 'Coming out?' she said.

As I looked at her I could see the meatballs in the yard behind, just where they had landed the night before. No dogs had wanted them either. The light of day made them look like small brown sponges on the ground.

'Have you seen those things?' my friend said, noticing me staring at them. I walked on to the balcony.

'No,' I said innocently. 'What things?'

49

'Those brown things there,' she said, pointing. 'Nobody knows what they are, they just appeared.'

'Eeehhh – yes,' I said. 'They look horrible. What are they?'

'My mum thinks they're from outa space – she kicked one and it got stuck to her shoe. She had to shake her foot before it would come off.' My friend screwed up her face and I screwed up mine.

'Urghh – they're horrible.' I hoped I was convincing.

I watched people walk through the yard and point at the meatballs and mutter. A dog came and I thought, 'At last they'll be eaten.' But it just sniffed one or two of them and ran away.

'What are they?' I heard two neighbours say as they came along the balcony. 'We'll have to get the caretaker!'

Just as they reached our front door my dad appeared in the doorway. I felt my face flush red.

'Mr Jacobs,' one of the neighbours said, 'have you seen those things in the yard?'

I wanted to block up my ears. I didn't want to hear my dad say, 'What, our old meatballs?' He came out on to the balcony and looked steadily down into the yard. Then he said, 'Oh dear . . . what are they?'

'We don't know, they were just there.'

'I think someone must have thrown them out,' the other neighbour added. Everyone nodded in agreement.

'Cha,' my dad said, 'messing up the place like that.' He sucked his teeth and shook his head. 'Some people,' he sighed and smiled.

THE YARD

'Tin tan tommy – I see Sonia on the first floor!' I banged the old tin can up and down on the drain in the yard. The noise bounced off every wall and I shouted again, 'I see Sonia on the first floor – come on, Sonia, I've seen you!'

Sonia put her head above the balcony ledge and shouted down to me, 'You couldn't have.'

'I did!' I shouted back. 'You're there – come on, you're out.'

As Sonia ran past my flat on the ground floor, she stopped as she heard the familiar sound of my dad tapping on our kitchen window. We both looked and saw my dad holding up the curtain with one hand and flicking his other hand in the air. 'Don't make so much noise. Stop that noise or get away!' he called through the closed window.

Sonia walked slowly towards me with her head down.

'Why's your dad always do that?' she said with a sulky voice.

'I don't know,' I said, trying not to look embarrassed. 'It's just that someone broke our window the other day. You can see. See that cardboard in the door window, that's where someone broke it.'

Sonia looked at the door, unimpressed. 'He's always telling us to get away or be quiet. He doesn't own these flats. My mum says I can play where I want.'

I looked to the kitchen window again and saw my dad straining his neck to see what we were doing.

'Well, shall we play something else?' I suggested.

'Your dad always spoils it,' Sonia said.

Christine poked her head over the top-floor balcony. 'Are we still playing?' she yelled.

'No – come down,' Sonia called back.

When Christine reached my kitchen window the tapping started again. She slowed down and walked towards us.

'Angela's dad's there,' Sonia said. We all looked to the window.

'We weren't doing anything,' Christine said to me. 'Why's he always telling us off?'

'Don't know,' I said, turning my back away from the window.

'He's such a spoilsport,' Sonia said.

'It's 'cause someone broke our window with a ball,' I said again in my defence.

'*We* didn't – we don't even know who did,' Sonia stated, with her hands on her hips.

'We haven't even got a ball,' Christine joined in. 'We can't even break the window now.'

We looked to the kitchen window again. The curtain was down but I could see my dad's figure behind it.

'I'm going in,' Sonia said. 'You can come and play at my house if you want, Christine!' They both gave me a dirty look and walked off.

I pretended not to care. I picked up the tin can and looked at it. I put it on the floor and kicked it a little way trying not to make any noise. Christine and Sonia were out of sight but I could hear them giggling as they walked up the stairwell.

Then I heard the sound of running. I turned round quickly and saw a huge black dog, almost my height standing in front of me. I was startled and jumped back a little. My sudden movement seemed to frighten the dog and it began to growl. Then it barked and jumped forward towards me, then back again, growling. I started to move slowly backwards but with every step I took the dog moved closer to me, showing me his teeth, snapping, growling and barking.

I began to shake and cry and froze on the spot. Suddenly the front door of our flat opened and my dad sprang out. With one movement he put his hand on the railings and leapt over the balcony and dropped down the eight feet into the yard. He scooped me off my feet then turned and shooed the dog away with his other hand. The dog gave a whimper then turned tail and ran.

I clung to my dad's neck and sobbed. He patted my

head and said, 'There, there – all gone,' and took me inside.

THE GAME

'Just whack it!' my brother called to me. 'Watch it comin', then whack it.' This was my third attempt to hit the ball with the cricket bat. It seemed too slim to do the job.

'She's not getting another go,' Ronnie called out.

'She's only small,' my brother protested limply. 'Just whack it, Angela!' he yelled to me again.

I saw the ball coming towards me. I wished hard. Then I felt it strike against the bat as I swung it around in the air.

'Yes!' my brother shouted. 'Run! run!'

In rounders you have to run to four bases. Base one was in the rounded corner of the yard of our flats, underneath the balcony near Colin's door. Base two was by the bins at the bottom of the yard. For base three you had to cross the yard to the brick pillar that stood out from the wall that separated the houses that backed on to the flats. Base four was the drain near the steps up to the balcony.

I ran, head down, not looking, touching base one, then base two as I went. As I ran across the yard to get base three my brother shouted, 'No! No! Stay!' But it was too late. As I got to the base the ball struck fiercely against the wall.

'Out!' Ronnie shouted, lifting his arms in the air. 'She's out – only you left,' he said, pointing at my brother.

'That wasn't out,' my brother shouted. 'She got there miles before the ball.'

'She never! I hit that ball straight on it – she never!'

'I did, I got there first,' I said. Ronnie took no notice of me. He didn't even look at me. My opinion didn't count, I was only Johnny's little sister. The game stopped and everyone came to base three to sort it out.

There were four people on each team. Our team was my brother and me, Peter from the first-floor balcony and Kathleen, who lived upstairs but had no mum. The other team was Steven, who lived round the block but always came to play round on 'our side' because he was a friend of Ronnie's; Linda, Kathleen's sister, who let people chew her bubble gum then put it back in her mouth; Brucie, who was a bit dim and slow; and Ronnie. Ronnie was the oldest and the biggest and everyone liked to do what Ronnie said.

All the kids that lived in our flats played out in the yard. We played until it got dark. Until mums or dads would appear in doorways and call someone in with the threat of a bath or teas going cold. We played 'cannon' and 'hee ball', where you had to get people out by throwing a ball and hitting them with it. Or 'run-outs' – a giant game of hide-and-seek, where your area to hide was Highbury. The game could go on for hours as we'd wander around streets, flats and parks, in twos and threes looking for the other team. When you found someone you hit them on the arm and took them back to the homebase, by the bins. We played rounders, peep-behind-the-curtain, tin tan tommy. The boys kicked footballs. And the girls put a ball in the end of a stocking then stood against the wall whacking it from side to side, under legs and arms, singing:

> 'Have a cup of tea sir.
> Yes sir. No sir. Why sir?
> 'Cause I caught a cold sir.
> Where d'you catch the cold sir?
> Up the North Pole sir.
> What you doing there sir?
> Catching polar bears sir.
> How many did you catch sir?
> One sir. Two sir. Three sir.
> And one caught me sir.'

But, if the ball hit your body or lost momentum you were 'out'. And we had shows in the porch and the boys would sit on the stairs in rows and the girls would sing 'Lipstick on your Collar', and dance.

This day Ronnie had suggested a game of rounders and said my brother could be captain of the other team. My brother and Ronnie picked their sides. I was the handicap – last to be picked and then I had to go on my brother's side because no one else would put up with a seven-year-old girl on their team. I had to play with them because Sonia couldn't come out as her Granny had come to stay.

'Well, she's out,' Ronnie said. 'There's only you now.'

'Get off – she got there first!' my brother said belligerently.

'She never,' Ronnie shouted. Usually Ronnie shouting was enough to stop any argument but my brother grabbed the bat from my hand.

'Let her have another go then – as a decider.' I cringed. I didn't think I could hit the ball again.

'No, she's out – your go,' Ronnie said.

My brother walked slowly over to take his go, and everybody took their places again. Ronnie threw the ball to him. My brother hit it high in the air then started to run. As he got to base three the ball thumped him on the back but he kept running. When he got to base four he held his arms in the air. 'Yeah – rounder!' he shouted.

'You're out,' Ronnie shouted. 'I got you out down there. I hit you out.'

'You hit *me*, you never hit the post,' my brother yelled back.

'So – you're out!'

'You have to hit the post, not me.'

'I don't – you're bloody out – you're all out, it's our go now,' Ronnie said angrily.

'No – it's my go,' my brother insisted, going to take up his batting position again.

Ronnie came up close to my brother and everyone else followed. 'You're out – give us the bat.' He went to grab the bat from my brother's hand but Johnny held on to it tightly.

'Give us the bat!' Ronnie screamed again.

'No – it's my go – I'm still in,' my brother said.

'You're out – I hit you out, you little cheat. Now give us the bat,' Ronnie said. The other members of Ronnie's team began to protest, but my brother stood firm on his spot. Ronnie pulled at the bat and my brother pulled back.

'Give us the bat,' Ronnie persisted with menace in his voice.

''S my bat,' my brother said, staring into Ronnie's face.

'So what, we're playing with it.'

'Well it's my bat and you're not playing with it if I'm out – I'm taking it in.'

'You can't take it in,' Ronnie yelled.

'I can.'

Ronnie grabbed at the bat again but my brother moved around with it, lifting it in the air. As he swung it, it hit Brucie on the side of the head and he yelped.

'You hit him,' Ronnie bawled, pushing at my brother's shoulders with both his hands.

'I never meant to,' my brother said, nodding himself forward again.

'You hit him,' Ronnie said, pushing Johnny again. I expected my brother to run. Nobody stood up to Ronnie. But he took a step back and held the bat up.

'Come on then,' he said, threatening Ronnie with the bat. The other kids went and stood behind Ronnie but I stood in disbelief at my brother's side.

Ronnie looked surprised then said, 'Come on then you little . . .' as he moved towards my brother. I started to cry. 'Come on,' Ronnie said, stepping nearer to my brother then skipping back again.

'Hit him, Ronnie!' Brucie said, still rubbing his ear.

'Hit him – he's just a golliwog.'

Ronnie looked round at Brucie and laughed, 'Yeah, come on you golliwog – you nig-nog – hit me with your bat.'

My brother lowered the bat and I started crying louder. 'Your little sister golliwog's crying, fuzzy. Better take her back to where you came from.'

'Take her back to the jungle,' Kathleen said as she put her hand over her mouth and laughed.

'Yeah, take her back to the jungle. You come from the jungle – all wogs come from the jungle.'

'Shut up,' my brother screamed. 'We don't.'

'You're not English – my dad said,' Steven joined in. 'He said you come over with all the other coons. You wanna go back, coming over here. You wanna go back – go back to where you came from – Blackie.'

My brother grabbed my arm and we started walking away.

'Nig-nogs – nig-nogs going back to the jungle,' our friends started chanting.

'Go on, Blackie – get back to where you came from!' Ronnie called after us.

'We don't play your games. You might eat us. Nig-nogs. You're all nig-nogs,' they sang after us and laughed as we walked up the stairs of the balcony to our front door.

We closed the door and heard a ball thud against it. 'Golliwog house, golliwog house – get back to where you came from.'

The noise of the ball brought my dad out of the front room. 'What's that noise? They playing with the ball near the door again,' my dad said, going into the kitchen to get a better look out of the window. I heard him tapping on the window then someone shouted, 'Coons,' and I heard them running away.

'Bloody kids,' my dad said as he came out of the kitchen. 'You don't play with a ball outside here, you hear me?' Then my dad looked at me. 'What you crying about?' he said without sympathy. We walked into the front room.

'What's the matter with you?' my mum asked in the same manner.

'What's the matter with her, Johnny? What you do to her?' my dad asked.

'Nothing,' John said.

'What is it then?' my dad went on. 'What 'appen?'

'Nothing,' my brother said.

'Don't give me nothing,' my dad said. 'She crying – don't give me nothing or you know what you'll get.'

My brother sat sullenly on a chair.

'What you crying about?' my dad said to me again.

'It's them out there,' I said, pointing towards the door. I looked at my brother who gave me a 'don't tell' look.

'What they do to you?' my mum asked. 'What they make you do?' My mum looked at my brother. 'You been making her show her belly button to them again – I told you I don't want them—'

'No!' my brother screamed.

'Good, 'cause I told you last time – it's nothing funny to look at.'

'I wasn't,' my brother said.

'They called us names,' I said.

'They call you names?' my mum said, looking at my brother. 'What names they call you?'

'They said we were golliwogs and nig-nogs.'

There was silence.

'Who say this?' my dad asked quietly.

'Ronnie and Brucie and everyone. They said we should go back to where we came from.'

'You should take no notice,' my mum said angrily. 'It's just stupidness. Just talk. Take no notice. You tell them you come from here. Take no notice.'

'I do tell them,' my brother replied.

'You don't have to answer them,' my mum went on.

'Just tell them to mind their business.'

'Yes, Anne,' my dad said, 'take no notice. You come from here. You don't let them worry you.'

'But we're different – we're coloured,' I said.

'Look, child,' my mum said. 'You born here. That's what matter. My mum always say to me, "You're not black and you're not white." That's what we are – we're not black and we're not white.'

'What are we then?' my brother asked.

'Cha, child – you're just you – you born here – you just tell them to mind their business. You have to learn to stand up for yourself. You're not black and you're not white.'

'They said we are coons,' I began to cry again.

'Then don't play with them if they call you that,' my mum said. 'You play by yourself. Take Patricia and Yvonne when they get back. You play with them. You don't need them. They don't want you. All those rough boys. You play by yourself.'

'They're my friends,' my brother insisted.

'How you have friends that call you names? They're not your friends. Friends don't call you names. You take no notice of them. Keep yourself to yourself,' my dad added.

My brother and I went to our bedroom, which faced on to the yard, and listened to everyone playing outside. If a ball came near our front door or anyone passed by our flat, someone would shout, 'You've caught the lurgy from the wogs' house – injected!' I could hear my friend Sonia now joining in and laughing. We sat, we didn't talk, we just listened.

'What's happened?' my sister Yvonne asked when she got home. She walked in with Patricia and my brother and I followed them into the front room. 'Everyone's calling us names,' she went on. 'What have we done? I don't understand. They're all saying nig-nog and Blackie.'

'Kathleen gave me a right dirty look,' Patricia said. They both looked shocked.

'Johnny had a fight with Ronnie,' I told them.

'You never!' they said together, staring at my brother incredulously. 'D'you hit him?'

'No, I never had a fight – shut up Angela,' my brother said.

'Well, what's happened then – why were they calling us names? I ain't done nothing. What's happened?' Yvonne said.

'You're to take no notice of them,' my mum said. 'They're just stupid nuh. Take no notice. Go and play by yourselves – together.'

'What!' Yvonne said, looking at me and sneering.

'We're not going to be able to go out again,' Patricia said with panic in her voice.

'Oh God!' Yvonne said. 'They're all out there – everyone. What we going to do? We'll have to move!'

'Move!' my mum shouted. 'Don't talk nonsense. Go out and play if you want to. Take no notice of them. Come!' my mum said angrily. She pushed at my brother with her finger then pulled him up from his chair. 'Come – go out and play – don't let them stop you. Come,' she said to all of us.

'No, I don't want to,' John said, pulling away from her.

'Come,' my mum insisted. 'They won't do anything with me there. Come now.'

'Go on – do as yer mum says,' my dad said as he lay on the settee with his eyes closed.

She went to the door and opened it. Everyone in the yard looked around and for a moment their game stopped. Then it started up again but with grins and nods going around. My mum stood in the doorway and beckoned my brother and sisters through. She stood there, large with her arms folded. My brother and sisters walked past her and sat on the balcony pretending to chat and look at something. I stood by my mum and looked at the other kids who began to move into a huddle.

'What's that smell?' someone said and they laughed. My mum pretended not to hear. We stayed there for ten minutes then went in.

The next morning, as everyone was milling around in the yard, my mum pushed us out again and took up her place in the doorway and I stood by her. Ronnie was kicking a ball to Steven and some of the other boys while Kathleen and Linda played two-ball against the wall. They looked at us but didn't say anything.

Sonia looked at me and smiled then gave me an exaggerated dirty look, moving her head sideways from my stare. I did the same. She came up on to the balcony and ran along in front of me. When she got to the porch, out of view of everyone else, she beckoned me and I went over to her. 'I am your friend, really – but pretend I'm not to everyone else – all right?' she whispered.

'All right,' I agreed and went to stand with my mum.

My brothers and sisters ventured down into the yard and began to set up the sticks for 'canon'. My mum still stood in the doorway. She nodded to the neighbours who had to pass our door on the way out of the flats and she commented on the weather and smiled.

As my brother stood in the yard, Ronnie kicked a ball to him as if by accident. My brother kicked it back.

'D'you wanna be in goal?' Ronnie said sheepishly.

My brother nodded.

Chapter 4

I visited my dad in hospital with my mum. He was sitting on his bed in his dressing gown, looking through a booklet on exercise that he'd been given.

'Dad,' I said excited, 'I designed that book.'

My dad looked at the cover and said, 'Oh,' in a nonchalant manner.

'Yes – I'm in it too!' I grabbed the book from him and flicked through the pages until I came to the picture of me skipping.

'Look, here Dad – it nearly killed me,' I said, turning to my mum who was adjusting herself into the only chair by the bed. My dad stared at the picture for a while and said, 'Oh – that you? You skip then?'

'Well, not exactly, but I designed the book you see so I did it for the photographer,' I said, trying to impress my dad.

My dad was not easily impressed. He didn't take much interest in the details of my 'career'. All he knew was that I had been to college and that made me knowledgeable about certain things – for example, whether milk was still good for you or not. The day before I went off to art college, my dad looked at me earnestly and said, 'So – what are you doing at college – typing and that?'

'No, it's art college,' I answered, and he had said, 'Oh,' in the same manner as he was saying it now, while thumbing through one of my designs.

He sat back on the bed and handed the book to my

mum. He then picked up a small rubber ball from his bedside table and began squeezing it with his malfunctioning hand.

'Has the physiotherapist been?' I said.

'Yes – nice woman, gave me this ball to get back me strength.'

'How was the X-ray?' I asked.

My dad's face contorted into a frown. 'Oh, nasty,' he said.

'Why?'

My mum interrupted. 'Look at that, Dad,' she said, pointing to a photograph in the book of a middle-aged man swimming. 'You could do that.' She began to laugh. My dad looked at the photo, tutted and began to laugh too. He then adjusted his pyjamas and dressing gown.

'What was it like then?' I continued.

'Nasty,' my dad said again. 'Long, and I couldn't move.' My mum pointed to another picture and they both laughed.

'What did the doctor say about it?' I said.

My mum tapped my dad on the leg before he had time to answer and said quietly, 'What's the matter with you, always fidgeting – you got ants in your pants?'

'What?' my dad said, moving his head closer to hers.

'I said,' she began, 'have you got ants in your pants?'

My dad looked at her briefly then they both began to giggle, and my dad repeated 'ants in your pants' with a mock show of disgust.

My dad was sent home from hospital the next day.

'They've given me some pills for the stroke,' he told me on the telephone.

'Are you feeling better?' I asked.

'Not so bad – bearing up. I'm eating though and I'm not smoking.'

'You've stopped smoking – that's great, Dad!'

I could feel my dad shrug his shoulders at the other end of the phone. 'I gave up in hospital, didn't I tell you? Just don't feel like them – no, I'm not smoking now.'

My dad had smoked for as long as I could remember. It was natural to see my dad with a cigarette. It was part of him like his arms or his moustache. I couldn't say how many cigarettes he smoked a day, but he'd buy a week's supply and bring them home in a brown paper bag, maybe twenty or thirty packets of Embassy Regal. He'd collect the tokens and we'd look through the catalogue to see what we could get. 'Just another two thousand tokens, Dad and you can get a torch.' Only after I left home did I realize that rooms and clothes didn't have to smell of stale cigarette smoke.

The hospital that my dad had been booked into to see the specialist was a long way from my parents' home. There was no direct bus or tube route. It could take one or two hours to get there and this was the hospital that my dad had to visit for his check-ups. So I said I'd take them in my car. It was a week since I'd last seen my dad. I walked into the kitchen and was astonished by what greeted me. The small grey man I remembered had turned into a fat man. My dad looked at me and smiled and I tried not to look shocked.

His face was bloated out as though he'd stuffed cake into his mouth and couldn't swallow it. His moustache hairs stood up and out. His head was the shape of a pear. His shirt was stretched across his body, putting a strain on the buttons and his cardigan which was once big and baggy, extended over his swollen frame. His arms looked like they could no longer fold across him and he limped more markedly with the new weight to carry. I couldn't recognize the physical man, but then he said, 'Hello Anne,' and patted my shoulder.

'Well, how are you feeling, Dad?' I asked, trying not to avert my eyes.

'Oh, much better – the pills are helping,' he said, steadying himself on the back of a chair.

'Good – what are the pills called?' I said as casually as I could.

'Steroids,' he said with authority. 'They build up your strength – like athletes take.'

My dad eased himself into a chair with the obvious discomfort of someone who can no longer bend in the middle. 'They make me hungry though and I've put on a bit of weight,' he said patting his stomach. 'But it's good – it's good.' He reached across the table towards a packet of cigarettes.

'I thought you'd given up?'

'I have,' he said, putting one to his lips. 'I only have one every now and again.'

The appointment at the hospital was with the chest clinic. I waited until my dad had been called in to see the specialist before I asked my mum, 'Why does Dad have to come to the chest clinic if he's had a stroke?'

'Don't know,' my mum said with a shrug. 'Just where they send him.'

I watched my dad walk painfully slowly back down the long corridor towards us. He smiled all the way but the discomfort showed as he dragged his leg.

'All right?' I said, walking up to him.

'Yeah – just got to stay with the pills.'

'What did they say about your weight?' my mum asked.

'They say I shouldn't eat so much.'

'Is that all – but did you tell them how hungry you get?' my mum said.

'No – no,' my dad answered, pulling a face like he'd smelt something bad. 'I didn't bother them with that.

They said everything was okay and they give me another X-ray on me chest.'

I looked at my mum but she turned away from me.

That evening I phoned my mum.

'I don't think Dad's had a stroke, Mum,' I said, after the preliminaries of how we both were.

'Oh, yes,' she said in the manner of someone whose conversation was being overheard.

'Is Dad there?'

'Oh no,' she said in exactly the same way.

'I don't think he had a stroke. It doesn't add up. Is that what the doctors said at the hospital?'

'Oh yes,' she said again.

'They said it was a stroke – but . . . but . . . did they tell you about the shadow on the lung?' I continued tentatively.

'Oh, yes.'

I had feeling that there was something she wanted to tell me and that I wasn't going to get much further on the phone.

'Will you write to me and tell me what they said,' I said, taking a chance.

'Oh, yes,' she said.

The letter came quite quickly.

Dear Angela,

Your dad went out shopping today. He bought an ironing board but he's had to give up ironing because his hands are too stiff. Gradually he's losing his grip on life.

The brain scan showed that the cancer had escaped to the brain and caused the paralysis on the left side. The doctor said that because of this they couldn't treat the cancer on the lung.

They wanted to know if they should tell him. I said

to wait a little longer. He's quite happy thinking he's had a stroke. I think if he knew the truth he'd just give up. Where there's life, there's hope.

I'm sorry to be the bearer of such bad news.

Love, Mum.

'I knew it,' I muttered to myself. 'I knew it.' Then gradually the satisfaction of being right gave way to a creeping nausea. I looked around me, frightened. I wanted to run and hide. But there was nowhere to go.

Chapter 5

THE HOLIDAY

We went on holiday by coach because it was cheaper than the train. But the journey was long, hot and tiring. We had packed all our clothes into one suitcase which swelled and groaned with a week's supply of outfits for two adults and four children. The blue suitcase had large expandable catches which reached their limit long before we sat on the case to shut it. By the time we had finished it was heavy, impossible for me to pick up, but then I was only a girl. No, this was a suitcase for a man to carry. It being our first holiday, my dad didn't know about the luxury that travel luggage could offer – for example, suitcase wheels were not something he'd come across. So it was left to my dad to carry the bag.

The first few yards were all right. He strutted out confidently, taking the suitcase in his stride and we were all relieved. But by the time we reached the tube station his face was red and sweaty. And he huffed and he puffed and he stopped to wipe his forehead. He'd carried the case for about 300 yards and I began to wonder how he'd ever get it to the coach.

I looked along the busy stretch of road that runs from Victoria tube station to Victoria coach station. It's about a quarter of a mile. But with our suitcase it seemed like a journey to the moon. My dad was now in a bad mood. His tie was undone and the top button of his shirt was open.

He didn't speak, he didn't moan, but he sucked his teeth and shooed my brother and sister away when they offered to carry the case between them.

I felt like the whole world was staring at us. A group of six struggling with a blue giant – stopping every five yards to huddle and make another plan. Then my dad had an idea. We all lifted the case on to his shoulder. He straightened and then lifted it on to his head. He smiled. It was a success – he could carry it like this.

From my vantage point, five feet behind the man with a suitcase on his head, I could see people pointing. He steadied the case with his hands but people moved out of his way as he walked past with an enforced momentum.

Thankfully, there were porters at the other end of our journey who had trolleys. The porter showed us to our chalet and dumped the suitcase at the door. He smiled at my dad, who smiled back at him. Gradually the porter's smile began to fade as it became obvious that no money was going to pass between them. He grabbed his trolley and left.

'You should have given him a tip,' my mum said.

'Cha,' my dad said with a wave of his hand.

Walking into the chalet was, for me, like walking into a palace. I rushed around the three-bedroomed mansion, opening doors and marvelling at every new room. I bumped into my brother and sisters and jostled with them for position in doorways.

'Look at the bathroom,' my brother said, pleased that he had spotted it first. 'It's got a wash-basin.' We all stood in the doorway and wondered at the sight.

Our bathroom at home was small with yellowy-brown gloss-painted walls. It had a bath and a gas geezer mounted on the wall, but no wash-basin. To wash, we would stand a bucket up on its end in the bath then put a basin on top. But the chalet bathroom was white and clean, with a toilet

70

next to the bath and neatly folded toilet paper. There was no wash basket piled high with soiled clothes waiting to be washed. No lines of dripping clothes over the bath. It was just a room dedicated to your cleanliness.

The bedrooms had two beds in each room, a dressing-table and a wardrobe. There were no clothes in heaps over the floor. No old cardboard boxes piled up, the contents of which were long since forgotten. No old TVs waiting for repair. No extra mattress with a hole in it waiting to be thrown out.

The kitchen was separated from the sitting room by a table and six chairs. I opened drawers and cupboards, which were full of clean cutlery, crockery, pots and pans. There were no crumbs in the cutlery tray. No cobwebs down the back of the cupboards. No dead beetles or silverfish in the bowls and pans.

The cooker lit automatically, you just turned the knob and it came on. There was a worktop, a long open plane of Formica where you could cut vegetables without food slipping down a crack and going mouldy. I ran my hands along it – smooth and cold.

Everything was white. The walls shone white, the floor sparkled white. Our excitement at our new temporary home was hard to contain, even for my parents.

The only complaint my dad had was that the huge picture-window, which ran the full length of the chalet sitting room, had no net curtain.

'Everyone can see your business,' my dad said. He looked in cupboards and in drawers for the nets. But gave up after a while. 'English people don't mind everyone seeing their business,' he finally acknowledged with a sigh.

We got a booklet at the holiday camp which told you about all the events that were going on that week – like a TV guide except it was real life.

Sunday 4.00 p.m. Donkey Derby in the field.
Sunday 5.00 p.m. Treasure Hunt for all the kids.
Monday 7.00 p.m. Glamorous Granny competition
  in the ballroom.
Tuesday 9.00 a.m. Miss Lovely Legs competition –
  come along and join in if you've got lovely legs.
Wednesday 1.00 p.m. Knobbly Knees competition
  in the Pelican Bar.

We all read the programme in turn, making a note of the things we'd like to see.

'Oh, there's a miming contest – I might go in for that. Dad, you should do the knobbly knees – you'd win.'

On the first night it said there would be a welcome in the ballroom at 7.30 p.m. for everyone who'd just arrived. So we got dressed up and went out.

I'd never been out with my family before in the evening. It seemed odd that at seven o'clock, instead of checking every channel on the telly for something to watch, we were all putting on our best clothes and combing our hair. But on holiday everything was meant to change.

My brother and I were ready first – we didn't seem to have as much to do as everyone else. My sisters were next, ready and keen in their mini-skirts and boots. Then my mum. We sat and waited for my dad who only got up from his reclining position on the settee when I was ready.

'Aren't you coming, Dad?' I asked him.

'Yeah – no rush.' He lifted himself off the settee like it was made of molasses.

'It says seven-thirty in the booklet,' I said.

'Well, no problem – don't get excited.'

We all waited for him, watching him tying his tie in the mirror and bobbing the lapels of his suit jacket into place.

'Come on, Dad – we'll miss it!' Yvonne said, tutting and chewing one of her fingernails.

'Ready now,' he said. He walked over to the picture-window and pulled the curtains across.

'It's still light, Dad. What you doing that for?' John asked as the room went dark.

'Don't want everyone looking in at our things,' my dad replied.

'You think anyone's going to want to steal this junk?' my brother said, looking around him. He laughed, so I laughed too.

'Go on, Dad,' my mum encouraged. 'It's a good idea.' She pulled a tissue out of her pocket and wiped it across her nose. 'I mind people seeing in, Dad – go on.'

My dad carefully closed the gap in the curtains so that not even the smallest spot of daylight came through it and nobody could press their eye up close to the window and peak in. 'Right – come on then,' he said when he was finished.

We walked out into the sun and my dad locked the chalet door behind us. My sisters walked on ahead. They didn't like to walk with us. I walked with my mum until I began to outpace her. My mum walked as if the hot Jamaican sun was still beating down on her and she had to conserve energy.

'Can't you walk any faster, Mum?' I asked. I often asked my mum this question when we went to the shops or were out together. And she always replied, 'There's no rush, is there?'

We walked past chalets and my dad smiled at any passer-by or someone who caught his eye and said, 'All right?' All the other chalet window curtains were open and you could see in. Every chalet was identical but every window showed a different life. Different things on the dining-table. Ketchup or Daddy's Sauce. Different furry animals and teddies on beds. Towels out to dry or whole lines of washing with nappies and swimming costumes. Different noises from each open door.

'Kenny, you get 'ere – you little . . .'

'Mum – where's my lilo . . .'

Hundreds of families packed tightly into the self-catering holiday homes. Packed closer than our flats. A home from home where everything stayed the same – washing and cooking. All strangers living on top of one another with one thing in common – we were having a good time.

Then we came to the large building where everyone congregated at night. We went through the doors to the dance hall area. As my sisters opened the door the smell of chips, people and alcohol hit us. There were people walking around or waiting, laughing and talking. There was an area with one-arm bandits and pinball machines that popped and cracked noise and light. People stood feeding the machines with money and standing back, hoping to have a win. There was a stall selling fish and chips and a long queue of children waiting, jangling handfuls of loose change or running about and falling down on the floor. The noise was deafening.

'Isn't it good?' I shouted. 'Can I have some chips, Dad?' I held out my hand for the money, getting carried away by the atmosphere.

'Cha – you've just eaten,' my dad said. 'You don't need chips.'

'Oh, go on – I'm hungry,' I persisted.

'You don't need chips – I haven't got money for chips,' my dad said, flicking his hand at me.

We walked on through to the double doors that led into the dance hall. The dance hall was a huge room that seemed to go on for ever, and it was crowded with people sitting round the edges of the dance floor. The lights were dim and the whole effect felt like something Cinderella would have seen. There was a silver ball high in the ceiling and the little flashes of light glided around the room. It had a beautiful wooden dance floor – polished and inviting. I wanted to run around it like the little children were, with my arms outstretched, leaping and jumping. At one end was a stage with a blue curtain with the Pontin name embroidered in gold, and with lights shining on it to brighten its glow. There was a bar at the back of the hall with bottles lit up by coloured lights. And two bars at the side behind glass walls which had tables and chairs you could sit at, away from the main entertainment. The bars had different names – the Pelican Bar, with a picture of a pelican over the door, and The Lodge, all wooden with scenes of mountains.

'Oh, isn't it exciting,' I said as we sat down. My sisters found us a table around the edge of the dance floor, near the back. But there weren't enough chairs around our table – we sat down, but my mum didn't have a seat.

'Here, Mum,' my dad said, getting up. 'Sit here.'

'No, Dad, you sit – I'll get another one,' she said looking around her.

'No, sit nuh,' my dad insisted. 'Sit, I'll just get . . .' My dad leant over to another chair nearby but it had a coat on it. 'No wait,' he said. 'Angela – no, Johnny, let your mum sit.'

My brother stood up and my mum sat down.

'Now I haven't got a seat,' my brother said.

'Well, sit . . .' my dad stood up from his chair again and looked around him. 'Angela, you sit here nuh man,' my dad said, patting his knee.

'I'm not sitting on your lap!' I cried.

'Just get another chair, Dad,' Patricia suggested.

'God, everyone's looking at us,' Yvonne said without moving her lips. She leant over to my dad. 'It so embarrassing,' she whispered.

'Embarrassing!' my dad said loudly. 'You and your embarrassing – *everything* is embarrassing to you.'

'I'll get another chair,' my brother said.

'No, Johnny you sit – sit.' My dad stood up and pushed Johnny down on to his seat. 'I'll get one.'

'Come Dad, don't make such a fuss,' my mum whispered.

My dad sucked his teeth. 'Who's making a fuss?' he said and sucked his teeth again louder.

We watched him walk from table to table in the crowded room. He'd point at a seat then someone would shake their head and my dad would move on. Eventually somebody nodded. My dad lifted the chair high into the air – way above people's heads. People ducked as he went passed them, scared he'd drop it.

'Oh God, he's so embarrassing,' Yvonne said, looking at Patricia. They both turned and looked in the other direction.

'There – got one,' my dad said triumphantly, as he approached our table. 'Move round nuh.' Nobody moved. 'Yvonne, move your chair nuh.' My sister tutted and rolled her eyes, then moved her chair a few inches.

'What?' my dad said, looking at Yvonne. 'You don't want me get the chair in?' He sucked his teeth. 'Cha, give me your cheek,' he muttered, too loudly for my sister, who turned her back to him.

'It's nice, huh – Anne – Mum – nice?' my dad said, grinning as he settled himself down on to his chair. My mum and I nodded.

'Can I have a drink, Dad?' I asked.

'A drink!' my dad said, surprised.

'Everyone's got a drink,' John said.

'You don't want a drink – you want a drink, Mum?' my dad asked.

My mum looked around her. 'Everyone seems to have a drink – maybe it's what you do,' she observed.

'Of course it's what you do,' Patricia said, rolling her eyes. 'We should all have a drink.'

'Well,' my dad said, looking uncomfortable and shifting on his seat, 'well, what you want then, Mum?'

My mum looked around her again, then leant forward,

closer to my dad. 'I don't know – what they have?'

'Anything,' Yvonne said.

'Well, I'll have . . .' my mum paused. 'I'll have . . .'

'Have a cola, Mum. That's what I'm going to have,' I suggested.

'All right, I'll have a cola.'

'You sure, Mum – you don't want anything stronger?'

'No Dad – no Dad – I'll just have a cola. But what you having?' she said.

'I don't know – I might have a beer – I'll see. What you want?' my dad asked, looking at my sisters.

'I'll have a port and lemon,' Yvonne said confidently.

'Me too,' Patricia added.

'What!' my dad screamed, with a look of pure terror on his face. 'You too young to be drinking – I'm not getting . . .' He became stuck for words.

'Oh, Dad,' my sisters said together.

'I have that all the time when we're out,' Yvonne carried on.

'You drinking when you out?' He looked at my mum. 'Drinking at your age. I don't like it. I don't want you drinking, you hear me? You go out to enjoy yourself, not go drinking at your age. You're too young, you hear me, too young.'

My sisters sighed.

'You hear me?' my dad shouted.

'Yes, yes, you don't have to shout,' Patricia said.

'Good – you hear me,' he said more calmly. 'You can have a cola like your mum.'

'I don't want a cola,' Patricia insisted.

'Don't give me any cheek,' my dad said, pointing a finger at her. 'Drinking at your age – it's not right. You want a cola, John?'

'Can I have a beer?' my brother asked.

'Don't you start,' my dad said, turning his finger on to John. 'You have a cola.'

My dad got up and went to the bar, and returned with five bottles of cola with straws and a half pint of lager.

'God, it's so embarrassing – I hope no one sees me drinking with a straw,' Yvonne said, putting her hand over her face.

'Who's going to see you?' my mum snapped. 'You and your embarrassing – no one knows you here.' She sipped at her drink.

'Well, cheers everyone,' my dad said with a grin as he sat down, but no one responded.

The curtains opened and all eyes turned toward the stage. The lights on the dance floor dimmed even more and the lights on the stage got brighter. There was a band on the stage. A drummer behind a gleaming silver drum kit, two guitarists and someone at a piano. Everyone clapped but the band didn't start to play. Then a man came on, dressed in a blue jacket with a bow tie. Everyone clapped louder.

'Welcome to Pontin's,' the man said into the microphone. His voice bounced around the room – loud and deep. 'We hope you'll all enjoy your stay with us. I'm Frankie, your host for the evening, and I want to hear a big hello from all those people who've been here before.' He held the microphone towards the audience and some people shouted 'Hello.'

'There aren't many of you, are there?' he said. 'Let's try it again – I'll say "Hello, campers" and you shout back "Hello, Frankie" . . . Hello, campers!'

'Hello, Frankie!' people shouted from around us.

'And now, all you first-timers. Hello, new campers!'

'Hello, Frankie.'

'Louder, new campers – let them hear you at home. Hello, new campers!'

'Hello, Frankie!' I looked around our table and shouted, 'Hello, Frankie!' and grinned. My mum and dad smiled, but my brother and sisters tutted.

'Well, let's start the dancing with a quick-step. Everybody who can, on your feet and everybody who can't – now's your chance to have a go.'

The band started playing. The music was loud and made my body tingle. People began to walk to the dance floor. Soon the floor was crowded with people dancing. Some gliding together like they were joined surgically – some watching their feet, laughing and giggling and looking around them as they moved around the hall.

'Do you want to dance, Mum?' I asked.

'No,' my mum said, shaking her head. 'I can't remember how to do this dancing. I forget now. We used to do this dancing in Jamaica though. You remember, Dad?'

My dad smiled.

'Do you want to dance then, Dad?' I asked.

'Me!' my dad said, surprised. He began to laugh. 'I can't dance.'

'Your dad can't dance,' my mum said, laughing. 'You could never dance, could you, Dad? He would never dance. No, your dad can't dance.'

'Well . . .' my dad said, 'I can dance a bit.'

'Shall we dance then?'

'No, I can't now, I'm too old,' he said. He took a puff of his cigarette. 'Johnny, you dance with your sister nuh?'

'Get off, I'm not dancing,' my brother said.

'Oh, go on,' I pleaded.

'No,' he said emphatically. I looked at my sisters, but didn't bother to ask.

The band played and the dancing went on – dance after dance. Frankie called out the name of every dance before the band started – names like the samba, waltz, tango, foxtrot. Then he shouted, 'It's the March of the Mods.' A little scream went up and suddenly young teenagers my sisters' age appeared on the dance floor. We watched. They got into lines and began to heel, toe, then jump together. I leant towards my sisters.

79

'Shall we do it?'

'No,' they said, watching intently. I sat back on my seat and sighed.

My brother suddenly stood up. 'I'm going to explore.'

'Can I come?' I asked.

'No – you can't go where I've got to go,' he said with a grin. He patted my head.

'Don't be long, son,' my mum said, 'and come back here, not to the chalet.'

I watched my brother weave his way through the crowds and out of the double doors. When I turned back there were two young people standing at our table. A boy and a girl. The girl was tall and thin with ginger hair in a neat short bob. The boy was much smaller than her with strange features that looked like somebody had shut a door on his face when he was very young.

'Do you want to come and sit with us?' the girl said to my sisters in a Northern accent. 'I'm Sandy and this is Ron.'

The boy smiled and his teeth pointed in different directions. 'We're over there with some others – come over.' My sisters looked at each other then nodded and got up from their chairs.

'We're just going to sit with them over there,' Patricia said, pointing to the spot.

'Where?' my dad said, straining his neck to see.

'Can I go too?' I asked.

'No,' Yvonne replied.

'Oh, go on, it's boring here,' I persisted.

'No,' Patricia said.

'Oh Dad, can I go?' I asked.

'Take your sister nuh?' my dad said.

'No,' they said together.

'We had her all afternoon,' Yvonne added.

'Oh, yes,' my dad conceded. 'Well, all right then – off you go,' he said, although my sisters had already gone.

I stood up and saw my sisters being introduced to a group of people, all their own age – boys and girls.

''S'not fair,' I said as I sat down again. 'They have all the fun.' I looked at my mum and dad who were looking towards the stage. My mum was tapping her head slightly to the music. My dad was smoking a cigarette, expressionless, and flicking ash in the ashtray. Then I looked around at the other tables. Everyone seemed to be really enjoying themselves. Families finishing off drinks and getting some more, laughing and dancing and telling jokes to one another.

After a few minutes even my sisters were on the dance floor. Everyone was enjoying themselves, except me.

'The Gay Gordons,' Frankie announced. My sisters were with two boys who were teaching them the steps, as they laughed and spun and tripped up and skipped.

'Look, they're dancing,' I said to my mum and dad.

'Oh yes,' my mum agreed.

'Let's dance!' I pleaded again as I looked between them. But they both shook their heads. I picked up my cola bottle and began to suck the last drops through the soggy straw but the straw collapsed mid-mouthful and I couldn't suck it up any more.

My dad spent most of the holiday curled up asleep on the sofa – just like weekends at home. He said, 'Nah,' when I asked him if he wanted to come to the amusement arcade at the camp. 'Nah' to the Knobbly Knees competition and 'What for?' to the donkey derby.

'You can't just sleep, Dad, you're on holiday!' I told him.

'I like to sleep – you go and enjoy yourself.'

One sunny day I was left alone with my dad.

'Come with me to the beach, Dad.'

'Nah,' he said, crinkling his nose and looking at me through one eye.

'Oh, go on Dad. You never come anywhere. It's not fair. I've got no one else to go with.'

'Go with a friend nuh?' he said.

'I haven't got any friends here. Dad – pleeese.'

'Well, go and make a friend,' he suggested.

'I want to go *now* Dad, while it's sunny. You haven't even been to the beach yet and we're on holiday.'

I persisted with my argument until my dad eventually said, 'All right then – stop yer nagging. You'll have to wait for me to change though.'

I smiled as I watched my dad haul himself from the sofa. I waited for fifteen minutes before my dad emerged from his bedroom. He was dressed in his grey suit. The only sign that he was about to take part in a leisure activity and not have a day at work was that he was not wearing a tie and had the top button of his shirt undone.

'You going like that, Dad?' I asked.

'Of course!' he insisted.

'To the *beach*, Dad?' I sneered.

'Cha – you nag me to go – do you want to go or not?'

'Why don't you leave your jacket, Dad – it'll get wet.'

'It's cold and windy. Come, let's go.'

The beach was crowded – full of English families. They looked like they'd been there a long time and had come to understand beach life. They had deck-chairs, windbreakers, radios, buckets and spades, thermos flasks and packets of sandwiches. They sat in the sun in their swimsuits and ran and splashed in the sea.

'Can we have deck-chairs, Dad?' I asked.

'No, they cost money. We can sit on towels – it's just as good,' my dad replied.

I walked to a spot in the sun near the sea, but as I was laying my towel down I could see my dad shaking his head.

'Not here, Anne – too exposed.'

'Where then!'

My dad pointed to a secluded spot, where the back of the ice-cream hut created the only shade on the beach.

'Not there, Dad – there's no sun.'

My dad sucked his teeth. 'All right, we'll sit here for a little while,' he said.

My dad laid out his towel and eased himself down on to it. He sat leaning on one arm, then he took out his cigarettes and lit one.

'Are you going in the sea, Dad?'

'Nah, too cold,' he said. He undid the second button on his shirt and leant back on both elbows. I'd never seen my dad in swimming trunks and just because I was on a beach in the sun with him, didn't mean I was going to now. I pulled off my dress and sat in my swimming costume.

'You go in, Anne, if you want to – I'll watch you from here.'

I paddled about in the sea but all I could see was my dad – a small patch of grey, on a beach of good time-candy-striped colours. He lifted up his arm and waved to me.

I came out of the sea and laid on my towel in the sun. After a few minutes I could feel water splashing on me. I opened one eye expecting to see a small boy playing too close. But I saw my dad standing over me. He had some water in his cupped hand and was flicking it over me with the other.

'What are you doing, Dad?' I shouted.

'That's enough sun now, Anne.'

'Get off,' I yelled, 'I've only just laid down, Dad.'

'Come, Anne,' my dad said, pulling at my towel. 'That's enough sun – it's not good for you, exposed like that – you'll burn up. Come, we'll go sit in the shade.' My dad grabbed the towel from under me and walked off to the spot at the back of the ice-cream hut. I followed him reluctantly.

'Sit here, Anne,' he said, laying out both the towels. 'And don't give me such a long face. You shouldn't sit in

83

the sun too long. You want to turn red like those English people – you shouldn't sit in the sun.'

'Everybody else—'

'Cha,' my dad insisted before I had time to finish. 'We're not like everybody else.'

Chapter 6

My dad began to walk with a stick, leaning on it heavily and dragging his leg behind him. His movements were getting slower. He stopped bothering trying to conceal his grey hair. Once he would have meticulously patted every grey inch with Morgan's Pomade and Brylcreem, but now he left it to its natural frizzy grey nature. He was ageing quickly, like a speeded-up film sequence, almost minute by minute.

'I've got this rash on me chest,' he said when I asked how he was. 'It's painful. Doctor give me some pills but it still paining me.'

I watched him ease himself into his armchair, flinching and holding his chest. But he held me away at arm's length when I tried to go near him. 'It's the rash – shingles or something, the doctor said.' He rested his head back and began to breathe deeply.

'What did the doctor give you?' I asked.

He pointed to a bottle of pills and I picked them up. Paracetamol. 'They're no good,' he said. 'They don't take away the pain.' He flinched again and took a sharp breath, then he shut his eyes.

'Shall I get you a cup of tea, Dad?' I said. I didn't know what else to do. I felt helpless. I wanted to do something. I wanted to take his pain away. I wanted him to smile at me and say, 'Hello, Anne,' like he always had before. I left the room and joined my mum in the kitchen.

'He's in a lot of pain, Mum,' I said.

My mum sat at the table peeling potatoes into a pan. 'I know,' she replied, without looking at me. I closed the kitchen door.

'I got your letter – thanks,' I said.

'Oh, yes,' she said in her way.

I filled the kettle with water, I wanted to be doing something when I asked her. 'Do you think we should tell him?'

My mum looked at me and said, 'Naah.' She screwed up her face as if the word hurt to say.

I didn't respond.

'Yer dad, Ange,' she carried on. 'Yer dad's not a strong man.' She said it tentatively in case I was shocked. She waited for my reaction but I just stared. 'He couldn't take it,' she explained. 'I've known him for thirty-eight years.' She looked into my face pleading for me to understand. 'I know if I told him, he'd just give up.' She began to pare away at a peeled potato. 'He'd just go downhill much quicker and I don't think I could cope with that.'

I poured water into the teapot. Her emotion and honesty embarrassed me. It was new between us. 'Do you want tea?' I asked, opening a cupboard door.

She shook her head. 'Well – we'd better not tell him then,' I said.

'It's for best. I'll tell him one day – I will – but not just yet, not at the moment,' she said.

I nodded and smiled at her. She looked relieved. I poured the tea.

'Did the doctor come here?' I asked.

'Yes – the poor chap's got shingles,' she said. It took me a moment to realize that she meant my dad.

'He gave him paracetamol,' I said.

'Umm,' she said, returning to her potatoes.

'Did he say anything about it?'

'No – he just looked at it and wrote out the prescription.'

'Does he know about Dad's other illness?' I continued.

'Yes, I think so,' she said.

'What did he say?'

'Oh, nothing,' she replied, unconcerned.

'Did you talk to him about it?'

'No – he's a busy man – always in a rush. I will one day but . . .' Her voice trailed away.

'But?' I said, prompting her.

'He's a nice man – you know – you can talk to him. I will one day.'

'Shall I go and talk to him?' I suggested.

My mum looked up at me, her face surprised, relieved and scared all at once. But she didn't say anything.

'What's his name? I'll go and see him. I'll try and get stronger pills.'

'He won't see you, just like that,' she said.

'I'll say I'm his daughter or you could come with me.'

'I can't, I'm too busy with your dad.'

'Well, I'll go if you like,' I offered.

'But,' my mum began, 'but you can't just go and see him. He's a busy man. He might not see you.' Her voice said 'go' and 'don't go' at the same time.

'Well, I can see if he will anyway – I'll ask Dad.'

'Suit yourself,' my mum said. I could tell that she was scared I'd make a fuss, scared I'd shame them.

I took the tea into my dad. He was sitting with his eyes closed and his mouth open. 'Dad,' I said quietly. He opened his eyes but did not move his head. 'I've brought your tea.'

'Thanks Anne,' he said, as he held out his hand to take the cup.

'Dad – would you like me to see the doctor for you? See if I can get some stronger pills for the pain?' He looked at me.

'Can you do that?' he asked.

'Yes,' I said with an uneasy confidence.

'Well, yes then, Anne.' He gave a flicker of a smile. 'You

87

talk to him. Yes, you go – you know how to talk to him –
you know what to say.'

I walked home with a heavy feeling in my chest. A burden.
I had asked my dad to rely on me and he'd accepted.

I knew this society better than my parents. My parents'
strategy was to keep as quiet as possible in the hope that
no one would know that they had sneaked into this
country. They wanted to be no bother at all. But I had
grown up in its English ways. I could confront it, rail
against it, fight it, because it was mine – a birthright.

But even through the years of grammar school and
college education; of gradually losing my cockney twang;
of eating lunch instead of dinner and supper instead of tea,
a learned fear of authority remained. Doctors frightened
me.

I went to the library and the Community Health Council
and armed myself with as much information as I could
about the services available to my dad. There was not very
much. But it was clear that the gateway to all services was
through a willing GP.

The doctor's surgery was a long way from my parents'
home. I wondered why they had registered with him as I
walked up and down the row of shops looking for the
surgery. Then I saw a handwritten notice in a window. *Dr
Karmen*, it said with a wobbly arrow pointing to the door.
I pushed the door and went in.

There was another handwritten notice saying
RECEPTION with another arrow, which pointed down
the long narrow corridor. I reached the door marked
RECEPTION and could hear a muffled conversation on
the other side. I waited. The surgery looked just a few
repairs away from derelict. All the woodwork was painted
brown and the once-beige patterned walls were stained
grey with neglect. It smelt of damp. The only light was

from a small window which was in need of a wash. It was like stepping back in time to the poor end of the 1930s.

I knocked on the door. A voice shouted, 'Please wait – I'll be just a minute.' After a few seconds a woman opened the top part of the door which was divided like a stable door. She rested her hands on the ledge this created and said, 'Can I help you?'

'I'm the daughter of Mr Jacobs. I would like to see Dr Karmen please.' I had been rehearsing these lines in the car all the way there.

'Are you registered?'

'No, I'm—'

She cut me off in mid-sentence. 'Well, you'll have to register. Do you live round here?' She turned and began sorting through some papers.

'No, I'd like to see him about my father, Mr Jacobs.' I put the stress on the word *father*, which always sounded so grand and middle-class. It was hard to imagine my dad as a father.

'Well, he's got someone with him at the moment,' she said. 'Take a seat – you can see him next.' She leaned out of the door and indicated down the hall.

I pushed at the door that said WAITING ROOM. The room was small with the same grey patterned walls as the hall. There were chairs placed neatly all around the walls and a brown wooden table in the centre with a few dog-eared magazines on it. There were posters and leaflets warning you of the dangers of things like smoking, eating sugar, measles, whooping cough. Most of them were from a different era when colour was brighter and all men had long hair and sideburns.

In the centre of one wall was a frosted glass door. I could see the shapes of two people moving on the other side. As I sat I could hear the consultation taking place. Athlete's foot around the genitals, sometimes known as dobbie itch. I hoped that nobody would come into the waiting room while I was in with the doctor.

It went quiet in the room and I could hear a pen scratching on paper.

'That should clear it up – but make sure you dry the area thoroughly,' a voice said. The shadows got bigger on the pane of glass and the door opened. A young man carrying a sports bag and a piece of paper came out. He looked at me and I looked away, embarrassed.

After a few minutes a voice called, 'Miss Jacobs,' and I went in.

The doctor was sitting in a chair at a large desk, which was cluttered with papers, pens, books and small models of parts of the anatomy. He looked out of place in the grey room – large and colourful in a dark blue suit with a white shirt and grey and pink striped tie. He wore glasses and his black-grey hair was slicked back on his head.

'What can I do for you, Miss . . .?' he checked a piece of paper on the desk. 'It is *Miss*?' he asked.

He swivelled his chair around and indicated for me to sit down.

'I've come about my father,' I said, moving into the chair. 'He's—'

'Oh, yes,' the doctor interrupted. He began to flick through the record cards which lay on the desk. He sat back on his chair. 'Yes, Miss Jacobs,' his voice dropped and he swivelled his chair towards me, looked me straight in the eyes and said with professional sympathy, 'I'm afraid your father is very ill.'

'I'm aware of that,' I said. I straightened my back so I sat higher in the chair, which was much lower than his.

'So what can I do for you?' he asked.

'Well,' I tried to remember, 'well, there are a few things.' He stared into my face and for a moment I couldn't remember who I was or why I was there. I took a deep breath. 'My father seems to be in a lot of pain – I

90

believe he's got shingles?' I said quickly.

'Yes, shingles,' he confirmed.

'Well, that's the first thing I wanted to ask. Is there any stronger pain relief he could get for that? He's in a great deal of pain and it seems a bit—'

'What did I give him?' The doctor interrupted, looking through the notes again.

'Paracetamol,' I said.

'Oh, yes,' he said. 'Well, there's not much else you can give for that.'

'But surely there is something stronger than paracetamol. I could have given him that,' I persisted.

The doctor bristled. Then he smiled, showing me nearly all of his teeth. 'You see, Miss Jacobs,' he said, 'do you know anything about shingles?' I didn't reply.

'You see, there is nothing really effective you can prescribe. There is a rash but the pain will come and go. It can be very intense, I know, but if I gave him something stronger he would have to take too many. You can't take painkillers for that sort of pain – it's very difficult.'

He stared down at me and I didn't know what to say. I was hostage to his greater knowledge. Then he started to scribble on a prescription pad. He tore off the paper. 'There, you can try this – it's a little bit stronger, but . . .' he said with a shrug, handing me the paper. 'Now is there anything else?'

'I wanted to ask whether my father could be booked into St Joseph's Hospice.'

'Oh, he's a long way off that,' he said emphatically.

'But it's a hospice, isn't it – for the terminally ill?' I said.

'Yes, but he would have to be a lot closer to the end before they would take him in.'

I was confused. 'How do you mean – how will we know if he's closer to the end?'

'He'll be in a sort of trance – almost a coma,' he said with indifference.

'Why couldn't they take him before?' I asked. The doctor looked discreetly at his watch, then back at me.

'They don't like to – anyway they couldn't now that he's got shingles. It's very contagious for people in that state. It would go through the place like wildfire. They wouldn't be able to take him until it had cleared up.'

He smiled a parting smile but I did not move.

'I was wondering about whether my mother could have a district nurse come to help with my father,' I said.

The doctor leaned back in his chair and began to swivel it again. 'Oh no – I think they live out of my area,' he said with a wave of his hand.

I straightened again. 'I think they're entitled to have a district nurse visit no matter where they live.'

He looked at me and smiled slowly. 'You're quite right, Miss Jacobs,' he said. He picked up the notes and began to look at them, then he turned back to me. 'The difficulty is that your parents live out of my area.' He looked at me and paused as if this was a statement that would clarify everything for me.

I stared at him and, after a few seconds of silence, said, 'Yes?'

He looked annoyed – he would have preferred me to say, 'Oh, I see,' and then politely leave.

'Well, I will have to see whether the nurse will visit your father out there,' he conceded. His impatience began to show.

I nodded.

'If not I will have to get the district nurse from their area to make the visits, which could take some time and organizing.' He looked at me again, hoping he'd changed my mind.

I smiled and said, 'Okay.'

'Why do you want a district nurse? Your father is quite lucid,' he said, scribbling a note.

'At the moment,' I said. 'But I want someone to keep an

eye on him so we'll know when it's time for him to go to the hospice.'

'Well, I'll do that,' he said.

'Yes, but we can't keep calling you out every week – can we?' I said.

The doctor shook his head. He picked up the phone and instructed his receptionist to contact the district nurse service.

'I wanted to know if there are any other services which might help my dad. Do you know of any? I've heard the Red Cross can—'

'No, I really think we've covered everything, Miss Jacobs, and I don't think the Red Cross can do anything.' He laughed. 'Now, is there anything else?' he said, looking openly at his watch, then me.

I wanted to say yes, yes, yes. What's going to happen? What will it be like? When will he die? What will he look like? Will he be in pain? What can we do? What can I do? I need help! But I just looked at this man and said, 'No, I think that's all.'

'Well, if you ring my receptionist tomorrow she can tell you what she has arranged with the district nurse service,' he said, getting up from his chair.

I nodded and stood up. I held out my hand for him to shake. He looked surprised, but shook it.

Chapter 7

THE DOCTOR

The doctor was called to me one day, but it was a day when only my dad was in. He tidied up the bedroom where I was. I watched him carefully make up the other bed in the room. He pushed as many toys and junk under the bed as he could, then skilfully laid the top cover on so as to conceal them. He took out stray clothes and put them in the wash basket.

'You all right, Anne?' he said to me every so often. I made small feeble sounds and my dad looked at me with concern and sympathy. He felt my head, then tucked in the covers on my bed – how I liked them – so I could hardly move.

There was a knock at the door.

'That'll be the doctor,' my dad said, as he made one last check of the room before going to the front door.

'Hello, Doctor,' I heard my dad say, but there was no reply. Then he said, 'She's this way.'

The doctor came into the room. Our doctor was a woman – Dr Kelmer. She was small and middle-aged. Everything about her seemed tight. Tight curls on her head. Tight clothes. She walked with small mincing steps and all her movements were precise. There was nothing unnecessary about her. Her form followed function. There was only one thing that stood out and that was that she had a permanent grin. She smiled without showing her teeth, all the time. The grin never got bigger and broke into a laugh. And it never got smaller even if she had something awful to tell you. She just constantly grinned the same, painful, tight smile.

She came over to my bed, pulled back the covers, grabbed my arm at the wrist and felt my pulse. She looked at her watch, grinning.

My dad had followed her into the room and was grinning too, to reflect what he thought was her mood. He winked at me as he stood behind her. She opened her bag, then shook a thermometer violently.

'Lift your tongue,' she said as she put it in my mouth. She then turned to my dad.

'All right, Doctor?' my dad asked with a broad smile.

'How long has she been like this?' she said.

'A few days, Doctor,' my dad said pleasantly.

She took the thermometer from my mouth, read it and shook it again. Then she leant over me and felt under my chin and ears. She didn't look at me but looked off into the distance, concentrating as she grinned.

'Open wide,' she said, shining a small torch down my throat. She clicked the torch off then pulled my bottom eyelids down. Then she stood up straight again.

'All right, Doctor?' my dad said again.

She looked at my dad and said, 'She's got tonsillitis and a high temperature.' She spoke like a school mistress, slowly and precisely, without pause, but she looked like the Cheshire Cat.

My dad's smile faded.

'You should have called me sooner. Two days you say she's been like this?'

My dad opened his mouth to answer but she carried on, 'Have you given her anything?'

'Disprin,' my dad replied sheepishly.

'Well, you should always call me if she gets a high temperature. She looks anaemic to me. I mean, what food do you give her? Is it good food?'

My dad looked confused and again went to speak.

'I hope she gets plenty of milk and fruit if you can't afford decent food. She looks anaemic – I'll have to take a blood test when she's a bit better. Do you understand? Plenty of milk.'

My dad, who had tried to persuade me to drink milk and eat up my greens for as long as I could remember, nodded his head.

'And this room,' she went on, 'this room is too noisy – you can hear everything that is going on outside. She needs a quieter room. Can't you put her somewhere else?' This was not said like a question that needed answering but like an indictment of neglect. My dad looked at the floor, unable to speak and the doctor looked at him, grinning.

'I'll give her a prescription for antibiotics. Now make sure she takes all of it. Do you understand, Mr Jacobs?' she said a little louder. 'All of it, not just half the bottle, and she'll have to stay wrapped up in bed. And try and open a window so it doesn't get so stuffy.'

'Yes, Doctor,' my dad managed to splutter like a scolded schoolboy.

She clicked her bag shut and handed my dad the prescription. 'Get it straight away, Mr Jacobs, and call me if she doesn't improve in a couple of days.'

My dad didn't reply. He just hung his head – cowed.

The doctor looked at me and I smiled back at her. Then she took a quick look round the room, shook her head, tutted and walked out.

My dad rushed behind her, trying to open the door for her but arriving too late and nearly being whacked in the face by it.

'Thank you, Doctor,' I heard him say and then the front door shut. My dad came into the room and he looked mad. He began to tuck my blankets in again and muttered to himself. 'Cheek of her – grinning at me all the time – grinning, grinning like sometin' wrong with her! Who she think she is?' He sucked his teeth furiously. 'She tell me me child's dead – she grin at me! Cha! Cheek! Come in my house tell me what to do! Who she think she is? Cha – grinning!'

He didn't look at me – he was in his own private fury. He tucked me in so tight that I couldn't move at all. Then he stood up and grabbed at a thermometer that the doctor must have accidentally left.

'Ha,' he said with excitement. 'Left her thermometer – good – ha. She's not getting it back – I'll have it – good!'

He put it in his pocket. For a moment he smiled to himself then started sucking his teeth again. 'Cha – stupid grinning woman!' he muttered over and over as he left the room.

'Dad!' I called from my blanket vice. 'Can I have some milk?'

THE LIGHT

One day my dad came home with a brown paper bag. I knew it couldn't be chocolate biscuits from the lady he knew because it was a Saturday. If my dad came home with a brown paper bag on a Saturday, it was because he had bought something he 'just couldn't resist'.

'What have you got, Dad?' I asked.

'It's lovely,' he said eagerly. 'I just couldn't resist.'

'Where'd you get it?'

'Umm – the cheap shop – a bargain.'

A bargain from the cheap shop was usually nothing to get excited about. The cheap shop was where my dad liked to get most of his things for the house, or Christmas or birthday presents. He liked it because, as the nickname implied, it was cheap. My dad never held with the notion of cheap and nasty or that something was cheap because it was crap and could only be sold for next to nothing. No, if it was cheaper than he thought it could have been, then he was pleased.

He unwrapped the paper bag and carefully lifted out the contents and placed it on top of the radiogram. It was a gold, domed building about the size of a shoebox. My dad then removed an electric lead which seemed to come out of one of the back doors and began to put a plug on it. He tightened up the plug then got down on his hands and knees and plugged it in. There was a click and suddenly the building glowed from the inside like some gold UFO.

'What is it, Dad?' I wanted to know.

'A light,' he said.

'No, I mean what building is it?'

'Not sure,' he mumbled. 'It's a surprise for your mum,' he said, smiling.

'Why, did she want one of these?'

'She wanted a light to read by – so I got this,' he said.

We both stared at the glowing building which was obviously a replica of somewhere. It had a balcony and hundreds of windows, but they were solid. It was like a jelly mould covered in gold. Only one small window in the centre near a balcony was open. As we stared at it, a tiny figure appeared in the window and then vanished again. I blinked.

'What was that, Dad?'

'What?' he said, trying to see where I was looking.

'Wait, look – in the window,' I said, grabbing his arm.

We both peered closely at the window. I was beginning to think I had imagined it when it popped up again.

'There!' I shouted.

'Oh,' my dad said. 'Didn't happen in the shop.'

I gripped him harder as we waited for it to come around once more.

'It looked like a pope, Dad.'

'Ehh,' my dad said, sticking his finger in the little window.

When it appeared again for the fourth time, I got a better look. It *was* a pope in full ceremonial costume, waving and smiling at us.

'It is the pope, Dad,' I said. 'It must be the Vatican.'

'Oh,' my dad said, 'I thought it was Buckingham Palace – you sure it's not the Queen?'

For a moment he looked disappointed, but then said, 'Oh, the Vatican – lovely.'

'But we're not Catholics, Dad,' I said.

He took no notice of my last observation but turned and rushed out of the room. 'I'll get yer mum,' he said as he closed the door.

I pushed at the glowing Vatican with my finger and a chip of gold paint flaked off and fell on top of the radiogram.

My mum came into the room smiling. Then she looked at the light and the little pope and said, 'But we're not Catholics.'

'Cha,' my dad said. 'Why should they have all the good things – it's lovely.'

'Yes, nice,' my mum said without conviction, and I nodded in agreement.

My mum tried to read by the light of the Vatican for about two weeks. Then one day the pope got stuck peek-a-booing, half in and half out of the window. After a while we smelt burning, then heard a pop and its light was extinguished for ever.

THE POCKET MONEY

My dad got up at his usual time, about ten. I offered to take his breakfast tray from the bed and put it in the kitchen. There was never much to do during the school holidays, so hanging around my dad and watching him get ready for work was, if not exciting, at least different.

I sat close by him on his bed. He rubbed my head but didn't speak.

'Let me do one of your shoes?' I said, as he got them from under the bed ready for their daily polish. He handed me a shoe and a yellow duster. I rubbed the shoe furiously with it and handed it back to him. He then brushed it with a polish brush.

'I've cleaned it, Dad!'

'I know, I know, I'm just finishing it off,' he said.

He stood up and took the shirt from the back of the chair where he had placed it the night before. He went to unbutton his pyjama top but then stopped and dug his hand far into his enormous trouser pocket. I could hear change jangling around in there, then he pulled out a sixpence and gave it to me.

'Here, Anne – that's for being good,' he said. 'Now go and play.'

I bounced out of the room clutching my earnings, and into my bedroom. I showed my brother, who was sitting on the floor counting pieces of Scalextric's track.

My brother didn't react in the way I thought he would. He wasn't happy for me, he didn't ask me how I was going to spend it and laugh and titter when I said I could buy, 'Oohh, probably 50,000 Mojo chews.'

'Why did he give it to you?' he said with a glum face.

'For being good,' I beamed.

'What do you mean, being good?'

I shrugged. At the age of six, I wasn't all that sure what constituted 'being good', but I knew I had been that day.

'Are *we* getting any?' he asked.

'You haven't been good,' I said.

'You always get . . .' my brother said, stomping out of the room. I could hear him telling my sisters about the money.

I went back to the comfort of my dad. He was standing

101

in front of the small shaving mirror which was on his chest of drawers, tilting his head at an angle which would allow him to see his hair in it. He patted his hair gently and pulled a small black comb through parts of it. Then he tilted his head again to see if he'd achieved the desired effect.

Suddenly my brother and sisters pushed open the door. 'We want some money, too!' they said, almost in unison.

My dad stopped patting his hair and looked at them.

'Money?' he said.

'Yeah – you gave *her* some,' my brother said, pointing an aggressive finger at me. I stood closer to my dad.

'Cha,' my dad said as he sucked his teeth. 'I don't have money to just give away.'

My brother and sisters stood firmly on their spot, hands on hips.

''*S not fair*,' they said. 'Why should she get some and not us?'

What started in unison soon became a cacophony of angry protest. 'She always gets . . . we never . . . 's not fair . . . what about . . . you never give us . . .'

Finally my dad shouted, 'Sschh – I don't have any money – now get out and go and play.'

My dad's voice dispersed them. I sat back on the bed and smiled at my dad.

'You don't have to tell everyone,' he said to me. I looked at the floor, then left the room.

My brother and sisters were in a huddle in the front room. My brother looked up at me as I walked in.

'Get lost,' he said. I stood in the doorway for a while longer trying to see what they were doing, until my brother shouted, 'Get lost – spoilt brat!' and threw a pencil at me.

I ran back to my dad. 'Dad,' I said, 'Johnny told me to get lost and threw something at me and it hurt.' I rubbed my head. My dad looked at me, then went to the door and shouted, 'Be nice to your sister or you definitely won't get anything.'

There was no reply. My dad looked back at me as I sat on the bed swinging my legs. 'Take no notice of them, Anne,' he said.

My dad opened his wardrobe door and picked a jacket off a hanger and flung it on the bed. Then he picked a tie from the selection that hung on the back of the door. He knotted the tie and put his jacket on, straightening and smoothing out the lapels.

'Right, I'm off now,' he said. He went over to the window and pushed it closed and swung the lock round.

'Be good, you hear,' he said, pointing a finger at me.

He opened the door of the room. There in front of him were my brother and sisters, blocking his exit. My sister, Yvonne, held up a table-tennis bat high in the air. It had drawings on it of my dad giving me money with the words IT'S NOT FAIR in big letters. My other sister and brother held up bits of paper with hastily scrawled WE SHOULD GET MONEY, TOO on it and more little drawings of me and my dad.

'What's all this?' my dad yelled.

'It's a protest,' Yvonne stated.

Then they began to walk around in front of my dad chanting, 'We want some money, too – we want some money, too.' Then the cacophony started again. I went and stood by my dad as my brother and sisters threw looks at me that could physically hurt.

My dad sucked his teeth and folded his arms. The protest went on until my dad shouted, 'Come – get out of my way – I'll be late for work.'

'What about our money?' they wailed.

My dad prised me from his leg and walked forward through them. He looked back. 'I was going to give you something till you made all this fuss.'

He opened the front door and shut it behind him. Then the letterbox opened and my dad shouted through it, 'You make sure you take good care of your sister now,' and left.

THE CHRISTMAS PRESENT

My dad got fed up with pine needles from the tree all over the floor at Christmas. You had to scoop them up and throw them out every day. And what did you do with the trunk and branches when it was finished with? Most people in our flats threw them into the yard where they'd stay for months because the bin men would refuse to take them. So it was decided to buy a plastic tree which we could use again.

My dad got the tree out of the cupboard about the same time every year. He blew the dust off it and generally flapped it about in the air. I used to help him when I was still young enough to be excited by Santa Claus and presents. He stood the tree in its red plastic container and weighed it down with a stone. Then he carefully pulled down every branch until it resembled the shape of a tree. As time went on this 'pulling down of branches' became hazardous, as they began to snap off with age.

'Oh, another one gone, Mum!' my dad would call out holding the orphan branch in his hand.

We packed our Christmas decorations into a box every year and when the tree came out, so did the box. It contained everything we had used to adorn the house the year before. The smiling Santa whose belly was made of red folded paper. The nativity scene with sprinkled glitter. The lanterns that you fanned open to reveal the many colours of metallic paper, and the Christmas-tree decorations.

When the tree was tree-shaped, my dad set about decorating it. He used a consistent method – he more or less remembered where everything had gone the year before.

'No, wait – that wasn't there,' he'd say to himself.

He put balls on the ends of branches. Balls that became so familiar that their celebration value waned. Then he'd lace metallic streamers around the trunk of the tree. They were blue and silver, and red and silver, although age made it hard to distinguish the two. There was tinsel next – limp, geriatric tinsel that tried hard to sparkle.

'We should get some new stuff, Dad.'

'This is good – it looks nice,' my dad would say.

Then came my dad's favourite bit. His *pièce de résistance*. His own artistic licence. Cotton-wool snow. He placed the little balls carefully at the base of each branch. He'd stand back, like an artist from an easel, then place another piece on to get the maximum realistic effect. The cotton wool got tired, became grey with age but still my dad insisted on putting it to work.

'I've got new cotton wool Dad, if you want?'

'No, this is good – nothing wrong with this.'

Then my dad would string up the lights and attach them to an old lamp stand. In a flash, the tree shone with bright, coloured lights and Christmas began.

Christmas presents were a problem, but getting a present my dad would like was a yearly challenge. Mostly I'd buy him socks or a lighter. He'd unwrap them with a straight face and say, 'Thanks, Anne.' Then he'd disappear into his room and I'd hear the bottom drawer of his chest of drawers being opened and I knew I'd failed. My dad's bottom drawer was where he stuffed all unwanted presents. Once something went in you generally never saw it again.

One year I bought him something too big to fit in a drawer. It was a plastic tool chest with brown and beige drawers that swung out. My dad was no great handyman and I wasn't even sure if he had any tools besides the electric screwdriver he used on the telly and Christmas-tree lights. But – it was a man's present.

My dad unwrapped it with his usual straight face. Then, slowly, a smile began to curl in the corners of his mouth, until he grinned, 'Oh, lovely – lovely!' He opened the catch and looked inside. 'Lovely drawers!' he exclaimed.

He swung the drawers back and forward, still grinning, 'Lovely, Anne, lovely.' He clipped the lid back. 'You know, Anne, I've always wanted one of these. I was going to get one the other day, but – oh it's lovely, Anne, lovely. Come, let me give you a kiss.' My dad rubbed his moustache against my face and sniffed. 'Lovely, Anne, thank you,' he said. He sat down again and opened up the tool kit once more. I was stunned and sat open-mouthed, watching my dad play.

The tool kit didn't go in the drawer – well, it couldn't. It went on top of the chest of drawers with the electric screwdriver in the first tray.

'I'll have to get some things to fill it up,' my dad said.

Then it was my turn to open the present from my dad.

'It's for your room,' my dad said, still glowing from his gift. 'A lovely plant.' It was plastic. A replica of a plant I didn't recognize. It had green leaves and a pink flower. The plant was pushed down into a plastic pot and held there by a dome-shaped piece of plastic, textured and green to resemble grass.

'It'll last a long time,' my dad said smiling.

That was what worried me, as I turned it around in the air to get a closer look. I held it by the stem, but then the plant came away from the pot and I was left holding the unidentifiable plant with a circular dome of green plastic halfway up it. My dad grabbed it from me.

'Oh dear – not to worry – I can fix it,' he said.

He took the plant and pushed it back in the pot. Then he fitted the 'grass' back in the groove until we heard a pop as all the air was expelled.

'There,' he said, 'lovely.'

After that present, I asked my dad if I could have money for Christmas. Money was a much safer option and it didn't last as long.

Chapter 8

My dad's stiff leg began to swell at the knee. It became red and puffy and he could no longer bend it properly. He found it harder and harder to get up the flight of stairs to his bedroom and getting dressed every morning became a strain. This, along with the shingles, had finally beaten him. He admitted defeat. He was definitely sick now. So he did what sick people do and took to his bed.

'I'm going to get yer dad one of those quilt things,' my mum said.

'A duvet?' I said.

'Yes, 'cause he's complaining about the blankets being too heavy on him. They're good, those things, aren't they – not so heavy,' she said, looking at me.

'Yes, they're great,' I agreed. 'You never have to make up a bed again.'

I gave a little laugh but my mum just said, 'They warm enough though – you think – for yer dad?'

'Oh, yes – get a high tog,' I said, flicking through the paper that was lying on the table.

'Tog?' my mum asked with alarm. I looked up into her anxious face.

'Just ask them for the warmest one they have – it's measured in togs but just ask for the warmest – about 13.5 I think.'

'Thirteen what?' she said.

'Oh, don't worry about that, Mum. Just ask for the warmest – really, I'm sure it will be all right,' I said, realizing I'd made it sound so complicated.

'You sure?' she said.

I gave a reassuring smile and nodded.

'Well,' she began tentatively, 'the trouble is, Ange, that the nurse rang this morning. The one from the doctor. She's coming about twelve.'

'What, the district nurse – oh, good,' I said.

'Could you let her in and that, Ange – only I've got to go to the shops.'

'Sure,' I said, 'no problem.' I didn't question why she had chosen that morning, at that time, to do her errand.

'You can show yer dad and explain everything.'

'Yes – don't worry,' I replied.

'Tell her about the knee,' she said carefully. 'Ask her if we should get the doctor to come and look.'

I nodded.

'And tell her,' she went on, 'tell her – well, see if she's got anything for his constipation.' She put on her coat. 'I won't be long – I might even be back before she gets here. I'll just say goodbye to yer dad.' She left in a hurry.

I began to make a cup of tea and then the doorbell rang. I opened the door. A woman stood there in a dark blue uniform with a coat wrapped loosely over the top of it. She was holding a clipboard.

'Jacobs?' she asked abruptly.

'Yes,' I said, opening the door wider to let her in.

'Sister Blackwell – district nurse,' she stated, as if reading from the board in front of her.

'Come in,' I said.

She walked past me, a small middle-aged woman with her hair pulled neatly back into a bun. She wore black tights and sensible regulation shoes. I showed her into the sitting room and she took a seat on the settee. I sat down opposite her.

She looked into my face for a moment, not speaking. I

could feel her instantly assess me, then she looked down at her clipboard.

'Who are you to the patient?' she said, like a shy child with a deed to do.

'I'm his daughter,' I answered. She wrote something down.

'Your father's full name?' she continued, without lifting her head.

'Winston Jacobs.'

'And where is he now?' she said, still writing.

'He's upstairs in bed,' I indicated.

'And what seems to be the matter with him?'

I went to answer, but she interrupted as she turned a sheet on her clipboard, 'Oh, he has cancer of the lung.'

I got up quickly and closed the door to the room. The house was small and an unusual voice seemed to bounce off every wall.

I looked at the nurse, who looked startled by my sudden movement. 'I'm sorry,' I explained quietly, 'it's just that I'm afraid he doesn't know he's got cancer – he thinks he's had a stroke.'

She looked puzzled. 'Oh,' she said, then she looked at her clipboard.

I hesitated. 'So – so don't tell him,' I said with a giggle.

'No,' she said, without lifting her head. 'Is there anything else I should know?'

'Well, he's got shingles and his knee has started to swell up and we're not sure what it is or whether to get the doctor.'

'Oh dear,' she said gravely. 'Well, I'd better see him.'

My dad was sitting up in bed, propped up on the pillows, looking pale and fat.

'The nurse is here, Dad,' I said quickly before she walked into the room.

My dad's face flickered into life as he patted his hair and

109

adjusted the top of his pyjamas. He pulled the blankets high up over his chest. I stood out of the way to let the nurse through.

'Mr Jacobs,' she said in a loud voice. 'I'm Sister Blackwell. How are you today?' She looked my dad confidently in the face.

'Not so good, sister,' my dad said, screwing up his face.

'Well, what's the trouble?' She leant down towards him.

'It's me chest – terrible pain,' he said.

'Let's have a look then.' The nurse grabbed for his pyjama buttons but my dad beat her to them. He opened the first three buttons and pulled at the fabric until he revealed a rash. The nurse peered closely at his chest then pushed a finger onto the rash. My dad flinched.

'Does it hurt now?' she asked.

'Comes and goes, sister, comes and goes,' my dad said, buttoning his pyjamas.

'And what about the knee?' she said.

My dad gave a look in my direction. 'Yes, me knee swollen up, sister.' He pulled at his covers and stuck his leg out from the side of the bed. He tried to grab at his pyjama leg but he was unable to bend the distance required. I moved forward to help him but the nurse bent down and vigorously pushed up the pyjama. They both looked at the knee, then the nurse pressed it in the same way she had pressed his rash.

'Is it painful, Mr Jacobs?'

'Throbs a bit, sister and it's hard to bend.' He strained over to rub his knee.

'Right,' the nurse said as she pulled down his pyjama leg. She pushed my dad's leg back under the covers and stood up.

'Anything else, Mr Jacobs?' she said, looking round the room.

My dad did not reply.

'There's the constipation,' I said from the corner of the room.

My dad looked at me again and I felt like I'd just betrayed him.

'Yes, sister,' he lowered his voice almost to a whisper. 'I haven't been for a few days now.'

'When was your last movement?' she said, leaning closer to him.

'Umm, Wednesday, no Tuesday,' he stumbled, anxious to be correct.

'Well, don't worry about that, Mr Jacobs,' she said loudly. 'I've got something in the car that will shift that straight away.' Her face briefly teetered on a smile.

My dad smiled at her. 'Thank you, sister,' he said.

'Now, is that all?' she said. 'No vomiting?'

My dad shook his head.

'And are you eating, Mr Jacobs?' she asked.

My dad nodded.

'Good – then I'll be back again,' she said as she began to leave the room. I smiled at my dad but he had rested his head back on the pillow and shut his eyes.

'Well, it doesn't look very good,' she said, looking at the ground as she resumed her position on the settee and picked up her clipboard.

'What do you mean?' I said.

'When they begin to swell up like that, it's not good – he won't have long.'

I wanted her to look at me. I wanted her to see that I was the daughter of that dying man – not someone with whom she could discuss another patient. But she didn't look up.

'Who said he had cancer?' she went on matter-of-factly.

I stared down at her, but did not answer.

111

'I don't think he's got cancer – he's too fat. When they're fat like that, it's not cancer – they get skinny with cancer.'

'The hospital said it,' I answered, going to shut the door. 'Please, keep your voice down.'

She looked up at me briefly. 'He's too fat for cancer,' she muttered to herself.

'He's on steroids,' I said emphatically but she did not respond.

'What do you want me to do?' she said after a pause.

'Well, what *do* you do?' I said, without thinking.

'Well, I could come and top and tail him. Do you live here with him?'

'No, my mum does,' I said, but the words 'top and tail' screamed through me. I wanted to ask her what it meant but she was still talking about something I could no longer hear. Top and tail him, I thought, top and tail him – isn't that what you do to runner beans?

I noticed the nurse stand up and I looked at her sullenly.

'I'll get the medicine for his constipation,' she said and walked out of the house leaving the door open.

I was scared – who had I forced on to my dad? The nurse returned and handed me a small brown bottle.

'That should shift it – the instructions are on it,' she said. 'I'll make a report and tell the doctor about the knee. He'll come if he thinks he should.'

I didn't look up at her but nodded.

'I'll be back either at the end of the week or the beginning of next,' she continued.

'Thank you,' I said, without thinking, as I showed her to the door and shut it behind her.

I went back upstairs to see my dad after the nurse had gone. I tiptoed quietly into the room and sat on the bed next to my dad's. He opened one eye, looked at me and shut it again.

'All right?' he said.

'How are you, Dad?'

He shrugged his shoulders. Then there was silence.

'What did you think of the nurse?' I said, trying to chat.

He shrugged again. 'All right,' he said, limply.

'She gave me the constipation stuff,' I said.

My dad opened his eyes and began to shift in the bed. He pulled himself up into a higher position.

'Pass me glasses,' he said, pointing to them lying on the table between the beds.

I handed him the glasses, then the medicine bottle. He looked at the bottle, holding it out away from him to read the small print. Then he took off the glasses and held the bottle further away, running his finger along the directions label.

'Two spoonfuls, it says here,' he said, looking at me.

I nodded. He put the bottle on the table and rested back on the pillows and shut his eyes. His glasses lay lightly in his hand, then gradually began to fall on to the bed. He looked exhausted, as if that small movement had drained him of all his energy.

'You all right, Dad?' I asked.

'No, Anne,' he replied.

I didn't expect to hear a response to that bland question and I certainly didn't want to hear a 'no'.

'Don't worry,' I said, into the silence. I looked around the room and focused on a tub of Brylcreem that sat on top of the chest of drawers. I began to remember the Brylcreem advert I'd seen on the tube. A young man trying to take the tired product upmarket.

My mind involuntarily wandered, then came back when I heard my dad say, 'When is it going to end, Anne? It's just one thing after another. When's it going to end?' He kept his eyes shut. I was thankful that he didn't look at me.

113

'It'll be all right soon, Dad,' I said, feeling feeble. I leant over and touched him on the arm. He opened his eyes briefly as he felt my unfamiliar contact, then he shut them again.

'I'll get a spoon for the stuff,' I said, getting up. He did not respond.

Chapter 9

THE RELATIONS

'What's she like, Dad?'

'I've told you, I haven't seen her for years – since we were young.'

'What *was* she like then?' I insisted.

'Wait an' see nuh – she'll be here soon enough.'

My aunt, my dad's sister, was coming to visit us from Jamaica and bringing her new husband, who was Scottish. Visitors were rare at our home, and preparations started almost from the minute my dad got the letter.

'Oh no, Mum, you know wha'?' my dad said, holding the letter high above the tray that held his evening meal. 'Doreen, me sister is comin'.'

'Comin' where?' my mum asked.

'She says she's goin' to Scotland to visit her husband's family but they'll be flying back from London Airport so she can come and see us.'

'Who's coming?' my sister Yvonne said, momentarily distracted from the television.

'Mind yer business, child,' my mum said. 'When, Dad – when she comin'?'

'Umm,' my dad scanned the letter, 'Sunday . . . it says here. Sunday . . . Sunday the twenty-fifth . . . that's . . .'

'But that's this Sunday – three days – you sure, Dad?'

'Who's coming?' my sister asked again.

'Yeah – who's coming?' I butted in and tried to grab

the letter from my dad's hand.

'Stop it, Anne!' my dad said firmly. 'This is serious! No – it say the twenty-fifth.'

'Let me see,' my mum said, holding out her hand for the letter. She read and began to look agitated. 'She could have given us more warnin'. All this time you've not seen her and then she just turn up.' My mum passed the letter back and my dad put his tray to one side as he read it again.

'Cha,' he said, shaking his head.

'Who's coming?' my sister shouted.

'Your auntie,' my dad said. 'Your auntie comin' from Jamaica.'

'She staying with us?' I asked. 'She going to stay here? She can have my bed – I don't mind. When she coming? – how long she going to stay?'

'Calm down, Anne, she not staying – just come to visit. How long you think she'll stay, Dad?' my mum asked.

'Couple hours.'

'We'll have to give them somethin' to eat,' my mum said as she looked into the air.

'They coming for tea?' I asked, all excited.

'What's her name?' Yvonne asked my dad.

'Who's coming?' my brother John interrupted.

'She's coming for tea,' I said to him. I got up and began to jump in the air. 'I can't wait.'

'Calm down, child, calm down,' my mum said, pulling at the hem of my dress. 'It's nothin' to get excited about.'

'Cha,' my dad said. 'Arsenal and Spurs on television Sunday.'

'Shut up everyone,' Patricia screamed from across the room. 'I can't hear the telly.'

My mum started cleaning and tidying the flat. She worked her way through each room. She dusted and hoovered places that had not seen a human for years. She worked her way through the linen basket until it was empty – washing every item right down to the bits of

116

clothing thrown in there years earlier, which were flat and dehydrated at the bottom. She got under beds, pulling out shoes and old socks and dusting them off. She washed the kitchen floor and put red polish on the front doorstep. She took down curtains and washed them and the windows. She spent several hours with her head in the gas cooker, cleaning and pulling out great black lumps of stuff that clung on to the inside being cooked over and over again.

'She's not going to look in the cooker, Mum,' Patricia said.

'It just needs a clean nuh,' my mum replied. 'Want the place to look nice – it justs needs a clean.'

We were made to put away all our clothes. I kept most of my clothes in a neat pile at the end of my bed. So did my brother. We had to sort through the pile and put things in drawers or wardrobes.

'I've been looking for that,' my brother said every few minutes as he sorted his pile.

'I like it better without the clothes on my bed,' I said when we'd finished. 'It's not so heavy on your feet when you're asleep. I'm going to always keep it like this!'

'No you won't,' my brother said.

'I will.'

He just looked at me and laughed.

My mum washed and ironed the clothes she wanted all her children to wear for the visit.

'I'm not wearing that!' Yvonne said, to the white blouse my mum had laid out for her.

'It's nice – you look so nice in it.'

'It's old-fashioned.'

'I made it for you,' my mum pleaded.

'Yeah – years ago,' Yvonne scowled.

'But you look so nice in it, nuh.'

'No, I'll wear this,' my sister held up a tight black polo-neck jumper.

'Nah – no – not that – so dark you look better in . . .'

She held up the blouse again.

'I'm not wearing it.'

'Cha,' my mum said, 'suit yourself – wear what you like – show me up with your ugly clothes!'

'I'm not wearing a tie!' my brother yelled from our bedroom.

My mum sucked her teeth and rolled her eyes.

On Sunday my mum and dad got up early. My mum spent the morning in the kitchen. My dad ironed a shirt then fluffed up cushions and put things straight in the front room. He turned on side lights, then stood back from them and looked at the effect. Then he turned one off again and then on. He opened the sash window six inches, then pushed it up two inches, then opened it a bit more.

'You all dress?' my mum said to her children as we sat around in the front room waiting for the big moment.

'You look nice, Ange, and you, John.' She looked at Patricia and Yvonne, who both had on mini-skirts and tight jumpers. She tutted.

'What?!' they shouted together.

'Nothing,' my mum said pointedly. 'Why can't you wear the good clothes I make? You children get so fussy when you grow up. You liked the things when you were little. Cha – fashion – look like – look like – like I don't know what . . .' She mumbled to herself as she opened up the leaf on the table. Then she brought in plate after plate of sandwiches and laid them down.

'Look at these,' she said with pride, pointing at a plate. 'You see these, Dad?'

'Oh, yes,' my dad replied.

'You see, they've got no top of bread.'

'Oh yes – no top,' my dad said absent-mindedly.

'It's because they're open sandwiches, you see.' She showed them around to everyone and everyone nodded.

'I got the idea,' she went on, 'when I was at Mrs Bennett's house – the Deputy Head at school. She had them and I thought – ah, I'll remember that. Looks posh, don't you think?'

'Just get less bread,' Patricia said. 'That's not really a sandwich.'

'It's an open sandwich – anyway, it adds a bit of style,' my mum said with a laugh.

She covered all the plates with white napkins 'to keep off the flies' and hide the delights from the guests until it was time to eat.

'Don't make me forget the jelly and fruit salad, I've got them in bowls in the kitchen. Remind me,' she said to no one and everyone.

'They soon come,' my dad said, looking at his watch. He adjusted his tie and straightened the lapels of his suit jacket. 'Now you all be good – you hear? No big lip.' We all rolled our eyes.

There was a knock at the door. My dad straightened his tie again and ran from the room. My mum took off her apron, folded it and checked round.

'Sit up, sit up!' she said, flicking her hand at all of us.

I jumped out of my seat to go to the door but my mum stopped me. 'Just sit and wait – leave yer dad.'

There was a great commotion at the door. Laughing and a voice saying, 'Oh, you've got fat – look at you – put on weight,' in a high-pitched Jamaican accent. I could hear my dad laughing. I looked at my brother and sister and smiled. My mum got up and opened the door and my aunt rushed in with her arms outstretched.

'Beryl, Beryl!' she screamed as she grabbed my mum and hugged her fiercely. She was a tall, thin woman but her presence was large in the room. 'And these are the little ones,' she said to us. She looked like Yvonne. Her hair was neat on her head, black, and she smiled showing a row of perfect white teeth. She was young compared to my dad. She wore a floral, summer dress with a white cardigan thrown over her shoulders that looked too

119

summery for autumn in London. Her husband walked in behind her in his open-necked shirt and sandals. He was young and good-looking with his fair hair parted on one side.

'Let me look at you,' my aunt gushed. She grabbed John and turned him round this way and then the other. 'You must be Johnny – you're a big boy – look at you – red hair. Look Andrew, red hair, must be the Scottish in you. But I thought you were a baby. Ah my – but look at these big girls.'

My sisters smiled, embarrassed, and looked at their feet.

'So pretty – but wait – Winston, this one,' she said, holding Yvonne round the shoulders, 'you know who this one put me in mind of? Mummy!'

My dad grinned and shook his head vaguely. 'You think so?'

'Just like Mummy,' she said. She turned to Yvonne, 'you look just like your granny – just like her when she was young. Aah, my.' Then she looked at Patricia. 'Oh, you dark – not like your sister.' She gave her a hug and I watched Patricia's face flatten against her chest. 'Who you look like?' she said looking at her face again. Patricia smiled and patted at her hair. 'You must be like your mummy's side of the family,' she said, stroking gently at Patricia's hair too.

'And look at this little one,' she said, holding my shoulders, 'so pretty – look at this little one – you must be Patricia.'

'No,' my dad said, 'that's Angela – the baby.'

'Oh, the baby – the little baby. So cute – I heard about you, little baby. Come give me a hug.' She squeezed me tight, lifted me off the ground and swung me round a little. 'Look at this little one,' she said.

After a while we all took our seats in the room. There weren't enough chairs for me so I sat on the floor.

Everyone sat smiling at each other and for a moment there was total silence in the room until my dad said, 'So Doreen and umm . . . umm . . .'

'Andrew,' Doreen said.

'Andrew – how you enjoy yer stay?'

'It was lovely. We stayed with Andrew's parents in Glasgow. It was nice – we stayed with them and—'

'We did some travelling around,' Andrew interrupted. His accent was strange – part Jamaican, part Scottish. I had to listen carefully to understand him.

'Oh, travelled round,' my dad repeated.

'To the highlands,' Andrew said.

'Oh, that's lovely,' my mum said, but her accent had changed. She spoke like someone announcing a programme on television. I stared at her. 'I *love* the highlands,' she went on.

'You've been then, Beryl?' Andrew asked.

'Not for a long time,' my mum pronounced.

'Have I been, Mum?' I asked.

'No – before any of you were born,' my mum said, without looking at me. 'Did you like it, Doreen?' she went on quickly.

'It was beautiful, but too cold. This country is too cold. How you stand it being so cold?' my aunt shivered.

'I like it now,' my mum said. 'I enjoy the winter. Snow is lovely. Everything looks so beautiful – you should see it.'

'We saw some snow on the mountains,' my aunt said, 'soon as I saw it I thought, "I want to go home" – I like it hot.'

'It's not so bad,' my dad said, 'when you get used to it. At first . . . but it's not so bad. You have heating in the winter.'

'Ah, yes – I saw all the chimneys in the houses – some had smoke coming out – looked like little factories. Everyone has fire then?'

'Yes – some open fire with coal and some electric or gas,' my dad said.

'Must take a lot of money to keep you warm,' my aunt said, 'but this place is small – easy to keep warm I suppose?'

My dad shifted uneasily on his seat. 'Small, but cosy,' he laughed. My mum laughed too.

'Can I offer you a drink?' my mum said, standing.

'Something cold, Beryl, that would be nice. I'm thirsty from the journey,' my aunt said.

'Orange squash?' The guests nodded and my mum left the room.

'You think it's cold in this country?' my aunt asked my sisters, who were sharing a chair. They both giggled, shrugged their shoulders and dropped their heads.

'But you were born here,' my aunt went on, 'you don't know any different – it's in yer blood.' She laughed and looked at her husband. 'So how long you been living here then?' Doreen asked, looking around the room and shaking the cardigan from her shoulders.

'Oh, a few years now,' my dad said, 'but it's only temporary. We'll be moving soon. We want a bigger place.'

'We moving, Dad?' I shouted. My brother's mouth opened and my sisters looked at my dad. 'When we moving?'

'Soon – when we finish getting the money together – don't get excited,' my dad said quickly and threw me a look that said 'shut up.'

'So, what – you'll get a house?' Andrew asked.

'Oh, I think so – children are growing now they need more room.' My dad smiled over at us and we all stared at him. 'They need a room of their own.' I had never heard my dad say anything like this before.

'Where we going, Dad?' I asked.

'I'm talking to yer aunt and uncle, Angela. Be quiet, nuh.'

My mum came back with two glasses of squash on a silver tray with a cloth on. She handed down the tray first to Doreen then to Andrew.

'Can I have some, Mum?' I asked.

'In a minute, child,' she said, back in her normal voice as she sat down.

'So you like it in England then, Winston?' my uncle asked. 'No regrets about leaving Jamaica?'

My mum and dad shook their heads.

'No,' my dad said. 'It's good – life is easier – in Jamaica life is hard.'

'We hear you have no transport now,' my mum said.

'Oh, Beryl,' my aunt said, shaking her head slowly. 'Transport is bad – it's got much worse since you left, terrible, terrible. I won't use the bus.'

'You see, we have good buses and the tube here,' my mum said with pride. 'You can go anywhere.'

'Yes, I know,' my aunt said, 'you're lucky – we have to have a car.'

'Oh, you have a car!' my dad said, surprised.

'You have to, Winston – you can't get around. You have a car here?'

'No,' my dad said, 'we don't feel the need, do we Mum . . . Beryl? But it's hard in Jamaica.'

'It is . . . but you know, we have things now that we never had before you left,' my aunt said. 'We have washing machines now . . .'

My mum and dad sat nodding as my aunt continued, 'And we have television – you know we have television?'

'Oh, you have television?' my dad repeated.

'Yes, for a long time – only one station though.'

'Only one! We have three here. Angela, turn on the television, show your aunt the stations,' my dad said, pointing at the television. I turned it on. I pressed the

123

BBC1 button, then BBC2, then ITV. I left it on ITV but the picture began to roll.

'Turn it off now, Anne,' my dad said quickly. 'Three channels – getting colour soon.'

'We getting a colour telly, Dad?' I asked. My dad pretended not to hear me.

'Would you like something to eat?' my mum said. She began pulling the napkins off the sandwiches. 'Just help yourself – it's a buffet. Give your aunt and uncle a plate,' my mum told me. I stood up and handed them both a plate.

'This looks lovely, Beryl. You make it all?' my aunt asked.

'These are open sandwiches,' I said pointing.

'Don't point,' my mum said, grabbing my hand and laughing. The guests started choosing their food and my dad turned to my brother and sisters and beckoned them to sit up. My aunt and uncle sat down with their plates.

'Come,' my mum said to me and my brother and sisters, 'help yourselves now.'

'So, Winston, everyone back home sends their love,' my aunt said, 'they want to know when you're coming to visit.'

'Ah, I would, but with the children at school and working so hard . . . it's hard to find the time. But I hear it's rough there now.'

'It depends where you live, Winston – we don't find it too bad. It's rough but we don't get troubled,' Andrew said.

'You hear stories,' my aunt said, 'and it worry me. People with guns. I ask you. But we don't get it where we live.'

'Where you live now?' my dad asked.

'Barbican.'

My dad looked impressed. 'Oh, Barbican – still nice in Barbican?'

124

'We have a lovely house – you must come and stay – plenty room. Going up the hill a bit – you know – lovely. We have dogs to fight off everyone,' my aunt laughed.

'Barbican is lovely,' Andrew agreed.

'So, you working hard then, Winston?' my aunt laughed as she took a mouthful of food.

'What do you do, Winston?' Andrew asked. 'Doreen said it was something to do with telephones.'

'No, the Post Office – I work at the Post Office.'

I listened intently – maybe now I'd find out exactly what my dad did.

'What exactly do you do?' Andrew asked.

'In accounts. I work in accounts.'

'Oh yes,' Doreen said, 'you took yer exams here. I remember now, Winston. So you got a good job?'

My dad nodded. 'I couldn't have done that at home.'

'No, times were bad. It's hard now if you don't have proper qualifications,' my aunt said.

'What do you do, Andrew?' my mum asked.

'I'm a teacher at Campion.'

'Oh, it still going that school?' my dad laughed. 'That was a good school when I was there – still going. What you teach?'

'English and music,' Andrew said.

'Nice – Beryl teaching now you know.'

'But Beryl,' my aunt said, surprised, 'you were always a teacher in Jamaica – you had a good job!'

'I had to retrain when I came here.'

'Oh – I thought you got a job straight away. We kept saying back home that you'll be living the high life in England 'cos Beryl can always teach.'

'I'm teaching now,' my mum said, 'and I'm studying for a degree.'

'Oh, you always were the brainy one, Beryl,' my aunt said. 'How you teach and go to college too? I fill up all my time just around the house,' she laughed again.

'It's a correspondence course with the Open University. Quite good.'

'Well, Beryl, I take me hat off to you,' my aunt said. 'So you not missing back home, Beryl?'

'No, I have everything here,' my mum said.

'We hear awful things back home about how coloured people treated bad here. Living in one room. People not wantin' to give jobs if you from Jamaica. You find that?' my aunt asked.

'You find that,' my dad said, 'but we don't have any trouble. We just keep ourselves to ourselves. Don't let anyone know our business, you know.'

'It's the best way, Winston,' Andrew said. 'I've been out of this country for too long now.'

'So you staying in Jamaica?' my dad asked.

'I like it, Winston, can't think of a reason to leave – although my mum would like me to come back. But I'm a Jamaican now.'

'I love me little Jamaica – it's home,' Doreen said.

'Well, I have everything I need just here,' my mum repeated. Just as she did, all the lights went out in the room.

'Oh what 'appen?' my aunt said.

My dad got up from his seat quickly and ran from the room.

'The two shillings has gone in the meter,' I told my aunt.

'What?' she said, puzzled.

'You have to put two shillings in the meter or all the lights go out,' I explained. 'It's run out – happens a lot, especially when you're watching telly.'

My dad called to my mum and she left the room too. My aunt and uncle sat eating. Then they started asking my brother and sisters about school. I could hear my mum and dad whispering in the hall, but still the lights didn't come on.

'Angela,' my dad called me. I went out.

'Angela – you have a two-shilling piece in yer piggy bank?'

'I don't know,' I said sullenly.

'Go and look,' my dad ordered.

'It's mine – if it's in my piggy bank, it's mine.'

'We just want to borrow it, child – come on,' my mum said.

'Haven't you got any?' I asked them.

'Cha, child!' my dad hissed through his teeth. 'Go and look!'

My uncle came into the hall. 'Is everything all right, Winston?' he asked.

'Yes, Andrew, it's just . . . it's just,' my dad hesitated, 'we don't seem to have a two-shilling piece for the meter. We usually have a pile ready, you see. They're coming to change this soon so we didn't bother to save up the pieces. I'll just go next door and see . . .'

'No, wait, Winston,' my uncle said, fiddling around in his pocket, 'I have some change here – look, one – there's two – take them.'

'Oh . . . well . . . if you're sure you can spare it. Here's the money.' My dad started counting out his change too.

'No, take them, Winston. We can't spend them any more now – take them.'

My dad clicked the money into the meter and the room lit up again.

'Sorry about that,' my dad said to my aunt as he sat back down in the room. 'We're changing it soon.'

We all sat and ate. Then my aunt said, 'Well, we're going to have to love you and leave you, I'm afraid.'

'So soon?' my mum said.

'We have to get back to the hotel.'

'Hotel!' my mum said, startled. 'You staying in a hotel?'

'Just for tonight – it's near the airport. Beryl, you know what time our flight? Tell them, Andrew.'

'Six thirty a.m.,' Andrew said, laughing.

'That's early,' my mum said, and my dad blew out breath heavily.

'So we have to get back and try to get some sleep. It's been lovely to see you. We couldn't have gone without seeing you. Everyone back home want to know how you getting on. Now we can tell them.'

My aunt and uncle stood up and we all followed.

'Wait!' my aunt said. 'Where the parcel?'

'In the hall,' Andrew said, leaving the room. He came back with a brown parcel. 'We've been carrying this everywhere for you,' he said.

'It would be just like me to forget it,' my aunt said.

'What is it?' my mum asked.

'Something to remind you of home – a Christmas cake,' my aunt said with a smile. 'And some other bits an' pieces we collect up – I can't remember now.'

'Is there something for me?' I asked.

'Schh,' my dad said to me.

'I'm sure there's something for you, little one,' my aunt cooed. 'She not shy this one,' she said, pulling my cheek. My uncle put his hand in his trouser pocket and handed me and my brother and sisters a two and sixpenny piece each.

'Ah, you shouldn't,' my dad said. 'They get plenty pocket money from me.'

'No, we don't,' I said, but no one seemed to hear.

'Hope we see you in Jamaica,' my aunt said, moving towards the door. 'It's been lovely, and lovely food, Beryl.'

My aunt and uncle stood on the balcony. 'Lovely to see you – see you in Jamaica,' they shouted as they waved. My dad flinched and looked out to see if anyone was looking, then he smiled. We all waved to them and said 'Goodbye.'

Then my mum said, 'Oh no, you know what!?' We all looked at her. 'I forget the jelly and fruit salad.'

Chapter 10

'They've taken your dad to hospital,' my mum's voice said over the telephone.

'When, why?' I responded, dazed. Only seconds earlier I had been discussing the merits of the Plantin typeface over Gill sans light and whether a 2,000 print run in one colour would be better than 1,000 in two, but the phone call switched me like a traffic light, from green to red.

'The doctor came,' she said.

'What, for his chest?'

'No, his knee – it swelled right up and started to give him pain.'

'What did the doctor say?' I asked.

'He didn't say anything,' she said, 'he just said that he thought he should go into hospital so they can keep an eye on it.'

'What hospital?'

'Same as before. They came and took us in an ambulance. It was so posh inside. I was surprised. You should have seen it, Ange. Everything neat. I think it must have been a new one,' she said.

'What ward is he on?' I reached for a pen.

'Same,' she said, 'they took him yesterday.'

'Yesterday!' I was surprised. 'Why didn't you tell me sooner?'

'I didn't want to bother you – I know you're busy,' she said. 'Anyway, I didn't know what ward he was on yesterday because I had to leave him in casuality.'

'Where?' I asked.

'Casuality.'

'It's casualty, Mum,' I said, correcting her pronunciation.

'Oh, yes,' she laughed, 'casualty – I don't know why I say casuality. Anyway, they were trying to find a space for him. He seemed quite happy though in his wheelchair. I had to get the bus before the schools came out. Those children – if you can call them that – they're so rough. I won't get on a bus with them.'

'So what's wrong with his leg – did you see him today?'

'Yes, I saw him. He's all right – a bit bored though, I think. He can't even do his crossword at the moment, poor chap. Do you think you'll go tonight, Ange?'

'Yes, yes,' I said.

'Only, could you come over and pick up some stuff for him? He's missing his food. I've put some biscuits and that in a bag.'

'Yeah, what time is visiting over?'

'Not until eight. You can go from eleven until eight, quite good really. One thing though, Ange,' my mum said hesitantly, 'as I was leaving this afternoon the sister stopped me. She said, "Mrs Jacobs, may I have a word with you." Quite posh – "may I have a word with you".' She imitated her voice. 'Anyway, I went in her office – Sister Tooke, that's her name – I had a few minutes.' She paused.

'Yes,' I said.

'Well, she says that your dad has a blood clot on his leg, that's what's making it swell like that.'

'A blood clot,' I repeated.

'Yes, but the thing she wanted to say to me,' my mum said quickly, 'was that I wasn't to be surprised if he . . .' she hesitated. 'She said the clot could move and I should be prepared if he just suddenly goes.'

'Oh,' I said quietly, trying to understand the words that

had just been spoken to me. 'What do you mean "if he goes"?'

'You know,' she said. There was a long silence.

'What, you mean he could just die?!'

'That's what she said. It could move, you see, and block somewhere else, in his heart maybe and he'd just pass away. I just thought I'd better warn you.'

I sat down and stared at the pile in the carpet.

'So don't be surprised, Ange – when you go tonight.'

'No, no. But did the nurse say it just like that, was that all she said?'

'Well, she was nice about it. She smiled, asked me if I wanted a cup of tea, but I'd just had one with yer dad – although you're not supposed to, it's meant to just be for the patients, but the woman gave me one anyway.'

'But how do you feel, Mum?'

'Oh, a bit funny, a bit funny,' she said, 'but that's life. "What the Lord giveth, the Lord taketh away".'

Chapter 11

THE NEIGHBOURS

'Where you goin', Ange?' My mum caught me at the door
on my way out on Sunday afternoon.

'Up to Mrs Simpson,' I replied.

'Wait, wait – come here, Ange.' My mum beckoned me
into her bedroom. She sat down on the bed and patted the
space beside her. 'Sit here, Ange.' I sat down.

'If Mrs Simpson ask you what you had for your Sunday
dinner, what will you tell her?'

'Sausages,' I said.

'No, Ange, you can't say sausages.'

'But that's what we had,' I said, naïvely.

'No, Ange, you mustn't say we had sausages. We don't
normally have sausages. It was just today.'

'What's the matter with sausages?'

'No,' my mum snapped, 'you're not to say you had
sausages – say you had . . .' my mum looked into the air,
thinking. 'Say you had – chicken,' she said. 'Yeah, say you
had chicken.'

'But we had sausages!'

'Look, child – you're not going up to see her if you
say we had sausages. I mean, I know we had sausages
but it was unusual. I don't wan' that woman thinking that
we had sausages on Sunday – you hear? I mean, before
you know, everyone will think that we have sausages on
Sunday, that we can't afford to eat a proper Sunday

133

dinner. Don't say sausages – say chicken.'

'Chicken and what then?' I asked.

'Potatoes and peas. Say you had chicken, potatoes and peas.'

'What shall I say about the pudding?'

'You can say what you had, child – peaches and evaporated milk – but just don't make them think we have sausages on Sunday.'

'All right, can I go now?'

'All right, but what you going to say, Ange?'

'Chicken – chicken with potatoes and peas, then peaches and evaporated milk.'

'That's right, good girl. It's not lying, Ange – it's just . . . it's just . . . well, off you go.' She waved her hand towards the door. 'Don't stay too long though.'

Mrs Simpson lived in our flats. She lived with her husband George. She had no children of her own but she looked after me, after school and in the holidays. She didn't look after my brother or sisters because she said she couldn't manage all of us – only me.

Mrs Simpson was well-groomed. She had a pencil-thin nose, which supported a pair of horn-rimmed spectacles. Her blonde hair was always stiff on her head. It never moved, even in the most severe gusts of wind. It was a sculpted piece. George, on the other hand, had no hair at all or what he did have could be counted. He wore glasses like his wife's, which had special lenses that split in a half moon – some for reading, some for long distance. He was big and fat. She was prim and thin.

They lived in a flat identical to ours but that was where the similarity ended. Their flat was immaculately clean and tidy. Mrs Simpson's vacuum cleaner had a bag on the side that puffed like a giant lung. She pushed it round over all her carpets every day – a wheezing friend come to help her. She wiped and dusted quickly and furiously, like she had something to hide. Dirt and mess were her enemies.

'Have you washed your hands, Andy Pandy?' she said to me each day when I got home from school. 'Remember those germs. You don't know where your hands have been. You can't eat your bread and dripping without washing your hands, because all those germs will go down your throat and live in your tummy and give you tummy ache.'

The Simpsons were the first with everything. They had a television long before anyone else in the flats. Occasionally, they would invite people in to watch a programme, usually *Coronation Street*. They had a telephone that people would come and ask if they could borrow. They had a fridge and she would make ice cubes out of orange squash and give them to me to suck. They went to Spain for their holidays and started a collection of dolls in full Spanish national dress. And they had a car.

They took me out in the car to the seaside. We drove for hours and then as we neared the sea, George said, 'The sea's just over this hill. First one to see it gets an ice cream.' Then he stopped the car and ran to the brow of the hill and shouted, 'I can see it. I win!'

'Oh, you silly fool,' Mrs Simpson said, laughing. 'Isn't he a silly fool, Andy Pandy. I don't think we'll let him have an ice cream, do you?'

Then he got back in the car and drove it to the top of the hill and we all saw the sea.

My brother and sisters never came with us – it was just me and the Simpsons. They treated me like I was their child, and sometimes I wished I was.

On Friday nights George came home with his wage packet. Mrs Simpson always cooked a roast dinner on Friday night. I watched her from the afternoon, basting meat and turning crisp potatoes that I knew I'd never be able to eat because I had to go home for my tea. George sat down at the table and Mrs Simpson sat at the opposite end from him. I always sat in the middle.

'Not as much this week – I didn't get that overtime on Monday.' He slit open the brown envelope and laid the contents down on the table in front of him and began to count it.

'So, that's housekeeping,' he said, making piles in front of him, 'electric – petrol – Christmas Club – gas.' He went through everything the money had to buy.

'I've got to get a new pair of shoes and I want to get my hair done.'

'I don't know, not this week, eh?'

'Yes, George, this week.'

'Okay, we'll have to put less in the Christmas Club.'

When the money was fully counted out George turned to me and said, 'None left for Andy Pandy.' I smiled, then George took some coins from a pile and flicked them over to me at the table. 'No, we can't leave Andy Pandy out,' he said with his mischievous laugh. He pushed the housekeeping pile to Mrs Simpson and she pushed out the sixpences and gave them to me.

'Now don't put your hand to your mouth after handling money – you don't know where it's been.'

George put his hand to his mouth and pretended to faint, then laughed and rubbed my head.

'Time to go now, Andy Pandy,' Mrs Simpson said as she got up ready to serve the roast dinner. 'Your mum will think we've kidnapped you.'

When I got home my brother and sisters would ask, 'What have you got?' and I'd show them my pocket money from the Simpsons and they'd shout, 'Why do you get it and not us? 'S not fair!'

It was ''s not fair' that I got to go in the car to the seaside. It was ''s not fair' that I could watch television. It was ''s not fair' that I got to suck ice cubes and they didn't.

The Simpsons always kept their front door open, even

in winter. They had a curtain of coloured streamers that covered the gap. On this Sunday, like every other day, I walked straight in. But something was different. Nobody called, "Is that Andy Pandy?"

'I'm here,' I said after a while, but there was no answer. Then I heard shouting.

'I hate you! I hate you! I hate you!' Angry shouting. Voices raised like I'd never heard before.

'I hate you!' Mrs Simpson screamed.

'And I hate you,' came the deep voice of George. I hardly recognized it – it growled with anger.

'I'm leaving you, you hear me. I'm not staying here with you – you're mad, that's what you are – you're mad. I hate you and I'm leaving . . .'

'Go on then, leave, you silly cow. See if I care. Go on leave! I'd like it without ya – get some peace – leave, go on, sling yer hook now you stupid bitch . . .'

'Right, I'm leaving you – I'm leaving . . .' Mrs Simpson began to sob.

'Don't think crying will help, you stupid . . .'

'I hate you!'

'One day – one day I'm going to bloody kill you – you silly cow – I'll bloody kill you!'

'Yeah, go on then, do it then, go on then. Do me a favour, go on then.'

'I will – I'll bloody kill you . . .'

I froze to the spot, scared to move in case they heard. I had never heard George shout before, ever.

'Oh, shut up you stupid . . .' he screamed.

I sat back on the little table in the hall. I felt tears in my eyes. I moved my foot and a book fell off the table and on to the floor.

'Is that you, Andy Pandy?' I heard Mrs Simpson call.

'Yes,' I called feebly. I wiped my eyes with the back of my hand and stood up from the table. Mrs Simpson stuck her head out of the door of the room. She looked as she

137

always did, except she wiped her eyes and kept her head down, so I couldn't see her face clearly.

'Have you been there long?' she asked anxiously.

'I just came,' I said. George came out of the room, smiling. He looked the same, too.

'Have you been there long?' he said in the same manner. I shook my head.

'She just came, she said,' Mrs Simpson answered abruptly, without looking at her husband.

'I just came,' I repeated.

'Did you hear anything, Andy Pandy?' Mrs Simpson asked.

'No,' I said. 'Hear what?'

'Oh, nothing,' she said, smiling and shaking her head. 'Nothing – you didn't hear anything, you just got here.'

I nodded my head furiously. 'But I have to go now.' Then I turned and ran out before I had time to be stopped.

'You were quick,' my mum commented as I went in through the door. 'Did you say what I told you?'

'No, they weren't in,' I said.

THE SUNDAY SCHOOL

I used to go to church three times on Sundays. I went to the morning and evening services because I was in the choir. I wore a red cassock, white surplice, a white starched ruff round my neck and a red skullcap, which was held in place by hair clips. I came out of the vestry singing and holding a notebook and pen under the sleeves of my surplice so I could play 'hangman' or 'join the dots' during the long sermons. I was a soprano and we sang hymns and anthems for services, weddings and sometimes concerts. At Christmas, I sang the solo for 'Once in Royal David's City'. 'A real honour,' my mum had said.

On Sunday afternoons I went to Sunday school. The Sunday school was held in the church for the little congregation. Not little in numbers, but little in height. A lot of children from my primary school went, because it was the church school.

We took up the first three rows of the church pews and we sat, colourful in our Sunday bests, shifting on the wooden pews or running and jumping in the aisle. We made a lot of noise in the church – unfamiliar screaming and laughing, which echoed uneasily round the brown walls. When the vicar came in, he clapped his hands and it was all hushed again.

'Let us start with a chorus,' the vicar said. Our vicar was a round man – round face and round body, and he smiled a lot, which puffed out his pink cheeks. He stood in the front of the pews, dressed in his ordinary clothes and dog collar, not his black cassock that he wore for grown-up services. He began to sing, without accompaniment, 'Give me joy in my heart' and we all joined in.

Give me joy in my heart keep me burning
Give me joy in my heart I pray
Give me joy in my heart keep me burning
Keep me burning till the break of day.

As we sang we followed the vicar's actions – hand on heart, then arms outstretched – hand on heart, then pretend to pray – hand on heart, arms outstretched, then pretend to clap quietly. After that we sang the one about the foolish man who built his house on the sand. This had a lot of actions and was everyone's favourite. There were actions for the house, the sand, the rain, the floods and the house falling down. There were actions for the wise man, the house, the rock, the rains, the floods and the house staying firm. When we finished singing we sat down and listened to the vicar.

'You must be like the wise man and build yourself on solid ground in the love of the Lord Jesus Christ. Then when the rain comes in your life you can stand firm. Firm in His love.'

We shifted around, looked round at each other, pulled our socks up, compared our shoes, picked our noses, played with our hair and sometimes listened. The vicar didn't go on as long as he did for the adults, because after a while we began to talk.

When the vicar had finished, we had a prayer and we prayed for poor people in the world.

'Now, has anybody got anything they would like to entertain us with?' the vicar said after the prayer. He said this every week and someone would stand up and sing a song or tell a Bible story. I put my hand up. I'd been practising all week.

'Come on then, Angela, out to the front.'

I got up from my pew and walked to the front. I stood up straight with my hands behind my back and recited, 'Lo, I stand at the door and knock; if anyone hears My voice and opens the door, I will come in and sup with him and he with Me. Revelations three twenty.'

When I finished I looked round me and smiled.

'Very good,' the vicar said. Nobody was allowed to clap in church as it was ungodly. 'Very nice, and do you know what it means, Angela?'

I smiled and said, 'Umm.'

Then the vicar broke in, 'It means that God is always there and if anyone hears Him, then He will come into their hearts. Now, is there anyone else?'

There was a silence as everyone looked around them and up and down the pews. There was no one else so we broke up and went into our classes. The classes were so we could have lessons about the Bible and Jesus and were meant to be like school. But instead of a teacher who made you sit quietly and smacked you when you were naughty, we had Miss Thompson.

Miss Thompson was an old woman. Older than anyone else I knew. She had grey hair, which was parted in the middle and pulled back tight into a bun at the back of her head. She wore glasses and always carried a handbag, which she held over one arm as she stood with her arms folded across her stomach. She was a smiling Christian, a kind woman, whose expression of benign innocence looked permanently etched on her face. She loved little children she told us, and she used to be a missionary.

We were split into groups of four and followed Miss Thompson to a quiet bit of the church, trying to get away from the other groups. This week I was in a class with Sonia, from my flats – we liked to stay together. Michael, who was in our class at school, he was fat and was bullied by the big boys and would cry a lot and get bullied more. His dad didn't have a job. Michael hated church and Sunday school, but his mum made him go because she thought it was good for him. The fourth person was Ada.

Ada was black. She was also in my class at school. Me and Ada were the only black pupils in our class. And Ada's family were the only other black family that came to our church. Ada's family came from Africa. She had lots of brothers and sisters. Six, sometimes seven, who all came to the morning service with their mum, but never their dad.

Ada's mum was a big woman, friendly and talkative, who spoke in a broad African accent. People smiled politely as they talked to her and nodded but had the expression of not really understanding what she said. Ada's family dressed for church in white hats, socks and gloves, and satin dresses with sashes and bows. And the boys wore white shirts with bow ties and cummerbund waist bands on their trousers. Ada's mum sang hymns loudly, but Ada and her brothers and sisters hardly ever made a sound.

141

Ada had no friends at school and spent her playtimes with her sister, who was in the year below us. She sat politely upright through lessons, but had the habit of falling asleep with her head on her desk through stories and had to be woken up when she snored too loudly. Our teachers never asked Ada anything, because she would never reply – she just sat and smiled and looked embarrassed, but she was clever and got good marks.

This week I had a question for Miss Thompson. It was a question my brother asked me one night as we lay in bed. It was a good question that puzzled me, too, after he asked it. I told him that I would ask my Sunday school teacher and we both laughed.

As we sat down I put my hand up.

'Yes, Angela?' Miss Thompson said.

'Miss, I've got a question about the Bible,' I said. I couldn't help grinning.

Miss Thompson nodded.

'Go on, I'll see if I can answer it,' she laughed.

'Well, Miss, Adam and Eve were the first people on Earth,' I began.

'Yes, that's quite right, Angela. They lived in the Garden of Eden,' she said confidently.

'Well, they had two children, Cain and Abel.'

Miss Thompson nodded.

'And Cain killed Abel,' I went on.

Miss Thompson was still nodding and saying yes.

'Then Cain went off to the forest and found a wife,' I paused for dramatic effect, 'but where did she come from, Miss, 'cause there weren't any other people on the earth?'

'Oh,' Miss Thompson said, putting her hand up to the string of beads round her neck. 'Well, that's a good question.' I grinned and looked at Sonia, who pulled a face at my cheek.

'Well,' Miss Thompson went on, 'I'm not sure I know

the answer to that. Well, I mean . . . well . . . does anyone . . . well . . . no.' She began to go red. 'I'll have to think about that one,' she said. 'I'll tell you next week.' She looked along the pew at everyone else.

'Well, that was a good question, but let's start today by seeing what everyone had for their Sunday dinner.' The question she asked us every Sunday. Miss Thompson asked it with a smile on her face and her head tilted to one side. We went around. I said chicken – I always said chicken. Sonia said roast beef and Yorkshire pudding. Michael said crab, and looked at us all with a grin like he'd made it up. Then it was Ada's turn.

'What did you have, Ada?' Miss Thompson said, when Ada did not reply in the rhythm of turns. Ada sat with her head down, but her eyes swivelled and looked around her.

'What did you have, Ada?' Miss Thompson repeated. Ada's lips began to move as if she had just eaten something and wanted to get the grease off them. Miss Thompson leant closer to her.

'What did you have, Ada?' Sonia said. She touched her lightly on the arm and Ada lifted her head for a moment, then let it drop again. Then she lifted her eyes and whispered something nobody heard.

Michael tutted and puffed hard. Miss Thompson leant closer to Ada.

'Yes, Ada, just say it – what did you say?'

Ada's lips started to move again and she said, 'Sausages,' a little louder.

'Sausages,' Michael shouted. He began to laugh and Sonia put her hand over her mouth to stop her laughter. I just sat still.

'Sausages – that's very nice, Ada, but you know you could have said it louder so we could all hear,' Miss Thompson said.

'No, she couldn't,' Michael said quietly.

'Yes, you have a lovely voice, Ada. Everyone wants to hear your voice, Ada,' Miss Thompson said, tilting her head the other way and smiling.

'I don't want to. She's stupid,' Michael said.

'No, she is not,' Sonia said. 'She's cleverer than you – you're a dunce.'

'She's stupid and dirty,' Michael said, folding his arms defiantly.

'Michael, I don't think that's a very nice thing to say, especially in a church,' Miss Thompson said.

'She's dirty, Miss, all darkies are dirty. She's dirty,' Michael said again. I sat and waited. I knew what was coming next. It was the same at school. 'And so is she, Miss,' Michael said, pointing at me.

'She's not,' Sonia said. Michael grinned.

'You shouldn't say that – he shouldn't say that, Miss, he's always saying it. He shouldn't say that, should he – he'll get into trouble – he won't go to heaven, will he?' Sonia said enthusiastically.

I dropped my head like Ada and wished that the subject could change.

'Angela's my best friend, Miss – he shouldn't say that. She's not even proper coloured, Miss – it's just a suntan. Isn't it Angela, tell them,' Sonia insisted.

I nodded half-heartedly. Miss Thompson began to fiddle nervously with the buttons on her blouse.

'That's not a nice thing to say, Michael. I'm surprised at you, really I am. I thought you were such a nice boy – but to say such horrid things . . .' she became breathless.

'Well,' Michael said, 'she,' – pointing at me – 'is not quite as dirty as she is,' – pointing at Ada.

'You should shut up,' Sonia said, putting her arm around me.

'That's enough, that's enough now,' Miss Thompson said, clapping her hands.

As she did so the vicar called out for us all to go and sit

back for the final chorus. Miss Thompson left our pew and made her way down to the vicar. She looked flustered and upset as she spoke to him. He nodded his head and looked towards us.

I waited for Michael to take his seat, then went and sat on another pew.

'Take no notice of him,' Sonia said. 'He's fat anyway. It's just because no one likes him. Fat, greedy pig,' she said loudly. We laughed and sat down and Sonia poked her tongue out at Michael, although he didn't see. Ada went and sat on a pew by herself.

Miss Thompson left the vicar, who nodded and held his hands in the air to get silence.

'Now, Miss Thompson has been telling me some very distressing things,' the vicar began. My heart began to thump.

'She has told me that someone has been calling names. We don't have people calling names in the house of God. Come out to the front . . .' I waited for Michael's name to be called. Now, I thought, God will show him how wrong he is, how bad he is to hate difference. But the vicar said, 'Ada and Angela.'

At first I didn't move. I thought he'd made a mistake.

'Come on out to the front,' the vicar said, beckoning us. Sonia pushed me and I stood up and walked to the front. So did Ada, slowly. The vicar put his arm around me and Ada. Ada held her head firmly on her chest. I looked up around me and saw Michael grinning. Then I dropped my head, too.

'Now Ada and Angela and their families are coloured, but that doesn't make them any different to you or me. We are all God's children and in the sight of God, everyone is equal. Now we will sing the chorus together.' The vicar held on tight to me so I couldn't go back to my seat. Then he began to sing, 'Jesus loves the little children.'

And everyone joined in.

'Jesus loves the little children
All the children of the world
Black and yellow, red and white
All are precious in His sight
Jesus loves the little children of the world.'

When we had finished, the vicar said, 'And again.'
Everyone sang the chorus again and the vicar looked
down at me and Ada. When the chorus was finished the
vicar patted us each on the head. Then he let us go.

Chapter 12

The hospital ward was familiar, although my dad wasn't waiting for me by the lift like before. I wandered through the warren of small rooms checking for any sign of him. I eventually came to the door of the long ward which kept about thirty patients neatly in rows. I had never been in this part before. It was for the people who needed to be watched. I looked up the row of beds and saw my dad at the far end sitting in a chair.

I walked towards him and saw that he was connected to a drip that hung above him like a guardian angel. As I looked I imagined him suddenly jumping up clutching his heart then falling to the ground with a crash. I imagined something dramatic, but he just sat by his bed in a blue hospital nightshirt with a bag of liquid attached to him.

'Hello, Dad.'

He looked up at me and smiled. He went to stand up but then stopped, realizing he was a sick man.

'Hello, Anne.' He sounded more cheerful than he had for a long time, as if the drip was pumping good humour into him.

'How are you?' I said, looking round for a chair.

'Get a chair from – no wait -' he went to stand again, then he sat back and tried to reach for a stool which was under the bed. His movements were fast and jerky and the stand above him started to wobble.

'No, Dad,' I shouted too loudly. 'I'll get it,' I said more quietly.

He sat back and breathed deeply. I pulled the stool out from under the bed and sat opposite him – eye to eye.

'How are you then?' I said again.

'Not so bad,' he replied, screwing up his face. He lifted his hand, which was covered in a large white plaster that had a tube coming out of it. 'I've got this drip.'

'What's it for?' I asked.

'Thins me blood they say – did yer mum tell you about me blood clot?'

It was hard to answer that simple question. Did they tell him everything about the blood clot or was it a secret, like the cancer?

'No, not really,' I said, after a pause.

'I've got this blood clot – that's what making me leg swell, you see – the drip thins me blood so it break up.'

He sounded pleased to be knowledgeable about it. In control. He stuck out his fat, bloated leg and rubbed it with his other hand, which was bruised black. The charred bruise extended from the back of his fingers to his wrist.

'What's happened to your hand?' I said quickly.

He held it up and turned it round in the air showing it to me from all sides. 'It's where they had the needle for the drip yesterday.'

'Does it hurt?' I said, touching it lightly.

'A bit,' he said, folding it away under his other arm. 'I'm glad you're here, Anne,' he added.

I felt myself blush. 'Well, Mum only phoned me today or I'd have come yesterday.'

'No, I'm glad you've come 'cause you can help me to the toilet,' he said without hesitation.

'What?'

He began to shift around on his seat.

'They give me this stuff, you see – to make me go – you know for me constipation,' he said, trying to stand. 'Only I can't go with this thing.'

He tugged at the tube that came from his hand. I

flinched. He grabbed at the drip stand which began to topple.

'No, wait, Dad,' I shouted as I steadied the stand with my hand. 'Wait a minute.'

'Well, quick, Anne 'cause I've got to go now,' he said at the top of his voice. I pushed him gently back down on to his seat.

'I'll get a nurse,' I said.

I ran along the ward but I couldn't see a nurse, not even in the room where they usually sit. Then I saw a man in a white coat. He was placing a thermometer into the mouth of a patient.

'Excuse me, have you seen the nurse?' I asked.

'I'm a nurse,' he said.

'Well, could you come and help my dad? He needs to go to the toilet urgently, but he's got a drip in his hand.'

'Who's that?' he said.

'Mr Jacobs,' I said in an urgent voice.

'Oh, right, we gave him something – right. Well, I'll be with you in a minute.'

'It's urgent,' I insisted. 'Isn't there anyone else?' The nurse looked at me slowly – everything he did and said seemed to go into slow motion.

'No, I'll be right there. I'll just finish up here,' he said.

I went back to my dad who was looking around anxiously.

'Is he coming?' he shouted.

'He said he'll be here soon,' I said, going to sit down.

'Cha,' my dad said with anger, 'I need to go *now*.'

He stood up again and began to walk away from the bedside. I grabbed at the stand and tried to pull it with him but it moved about a foot and then got stuck. My dad could walk no further.

'Just wait, Dad,' I said.

I couldn't really understand why it was so important, why he couldn't wait for just a minute.

He sat down again on the edge of his chair and jiggled

his legs up and down like a child.

'Where is he?' he shouted after a few seconds. 'It's coming!'

I ran back up the ward and found the nurse with the same patient.

'Please come,' I pleaded, 'he's desperate to go. I can't move the trolley.'

'I'll be there in a minute,' the nurse said impatiently. 'I have to finish up here first.' He looked at me like I was a selfish child wanting her own way.

I went back to my dad who was getting red in the face. I was scared he'd die.

'Where is he?' he screamed. He looked around him, looking for help. 'It's coming,' he shouted, getting up from his seat.

I looked around the ward. Everyone was staring at us. Then I saw the nurse walking slowly toward us.

'He's on his way,' I said with relief.

'All right, Mr Jacobs,' the nurse said as he approached.

'It's coming!' my dad shouted. 'Oh God, quick, it's coming.'

The panic in his voice made me start to cry. The nurse began to pull the curtain round the bed.

'Let it come then,' the nurse said.

'What, here!?' my dad said with disbelief.

'Yes.'

'On the chair – just let it come, nurse!?' my dad said anxiously.

The nurse nodded. My dad lifted his nightshirt over his genitals and sat back down on the chair. I turned away.

'You'd better go and wait in the waiting room,' the nurse suggested as he ushered me through the curtains.

I sat in the waiting room with the image of my dad playing itself to me over and over again. No matter what I looked at or what I read, I saw my dad lifting up his nightshirt ready to shit on the floor like a baby.

* * *

After about half an hour the nurse looked round the door of the room. 'You can see him now,' he said with a smile. 'He's all finished.'

I walked back down the ward. I could see my dad sitting up in bed, still attached to his drip. I felt embarrassed to approach him. Scared he'd turn his face away from me, away from the shame of what I'd seen. But he saw me coming and smiled.

'All done now Anne – come, sit,' he said, pointing to the chair. 'I feel better now.'

'Good,' I said, turning my face away from his smile. I stared round the ward trying to think of something to say next.

'Anne,' my dad said, 'they say I can come out in a couple of days.'

'Really?' I was surprised.

'But I don't know,' he went on, 'I don't want to, not with this drip and everything. Not till I know everything is going to be all right.'

I could feel his fear. 'Well, I'm sure they wouldn't send you home if they didn't think you were fit enough,' I chirped.

'Oh, I don't know, Anne, they need the beds. They say I can go home in a couple of days, but I'm not sure. I don't want something else to go wrong.' He began to shift restlessly on the bed.

'Don't worry, Dad,' I said, putting my hand on his arm, 'I'll go and see them – see what they say.'

He relaxed back on to the pillows. 'Yes, Anne, see what they say. Tell them I don't want to go before everything's all right.'

I knocked on the door of the room where the nurses and doctors sit, even though it was open. There was no answer. I put my head into the room and saw a young man

151

in a white coat sitting by one of the desks. The room was large and bright with a desk pressed against every wall.

'Can I help you?' he said. I had never seen him before.

'I'd like to talk to someone about Mr Jacobs,' I said.

'Oh, well, you'll want the ward sister. Sister Tooke.'

I remembered the name from the conversation with my mum. 'Yes, Sister Tooke,' I repeated.

Just as I said that a woman pushed past me into the room. She was small and wide in her pale uniform. She was unpinning her hat from her head. She threw the hat on to a desk as she walked past.

'Sister Tooke, someone wants a word with you,' the young man said, returning to what he was doing before I entered.

The woman looked at me. 'Yes?' she said.

I walked across to the other side of the room where she stood.

'I wanted to talk to you about my father,' I said. I stood over her, a good six inches taller than her. I tried to make myself smaller in case she felt intimidated.

'Who's that?' she said curtly.

I was surprised by her manner, but I smiled. 'It's Mr Jacobs.'

'Oh,' she said loudly, turning away from me. 'Old man Jacobs – what's his problem?'

I stared at the back of her head. I looked around the room. I saw the young man look up at me, then turn quickly away.

'*Mr* Jacobs,' I pronounced. 'Yes, Mr Jacobs.'

'Well, what is it?' she said, turning back to me. I could feel my face redden and my heart pound.

'He said that you're sending him home soon but—'

She didn't let me finish before she said, 'He's confused. He gets confused – take no notice.' She began to fiddle with the hair grips in her hair. 'Take no notice,' she repeated.

152

I could no longer speak. I picked up this little woman by her throat and held her up against the wall and slapped her. I screamed at her, 'Don't call my dad, "Old man Jacobs". It's *Mr* Jacobs to you, you bastard, you bitch. It's Mr Jacobs – my dad is not your plaything, not your annoyance.' I let her fall to the floor and then I picked her up again and threw her against the opposite wall and I kicked her and kicked her while she was down.

Then I heard her voice again and my fantasy ended. 'He's not going anywhere, not yet. Take no notice, they get like that,' she said as she walked out of the door.

Chapter 13

THE LITTLE GIRL

The ambulance driver used me to point with as he held me in his arms like a bale of cloth.

'Where d'you want her?' he said, pushing me forward. The nurse indicated into the long ward and then rubbed something out on the blackboard she stood beside. The lights were bright after the dark of the ambulance ride through night-time north London.

The ambulance had black windows from the outside but when I was lifted in I was surprised to find I could see out of them. There was another sick girl in the ambulance. I could tell she was sick because she had her nightie on, too. I smiled at her and she smiled back, but my mum said I was not to go near her because she had something contagious.

My mum told me that I had to be a big girl and not to cry, even when she left me in the hospital. She told me that the doctors and nurses would look after me, that they like little girls and that they would make me better. She told me I should be good and not give them any trouble. I had scarlet and rheumatic fever and I picked at the white paste that our doctor had painted on to my wrists. I wasn't sure what it was for and when I asked I got an answer no four year old could understand. Something about closing veins.

I was tucked up in the hospital bed by a nurse. My mum looked on, holding my slippers in her hand like two little birds. She put the slippers by the bed when the nurse had finished, then kissed my forehead and said she had to get back now.

'Now, be good – the nurses will take care of you. I soon come back,' she said.

I watched my mum walk slowly down the ward in her old brown coat. I didn't cry. I didn't want to. She disappeared through the double doors and I looked round the ward. It was filled with adults who all seemed to be coughing or wheezing or snoring open-mouthed on their beds. The girl from the ambulance was put in the bed next to me. But as they put her down they pulled a high glass partition round her. I could see her and smile but that was all.

I was alone. When they turned the main lights out in the ward, all that was left was the occasional light over a bed casting down on shadowy pale people. The noises were horrible. I wanted to hear the noises that were familiar to me; the sewing machine whirring up seams into the night, the television in another room, my brother and sisters laughing or arguing, my mum sniffing and my dad puffing. But all I could hear were clatters and bangs and coughing and wheezing and distant voices. I thought if I could only sleep then it would all go away.

Just as I was getting to sleep I felt a bright light shining on my closed eyes. I opened them and could just make out the shape of a woman dressed from head to toe in black. She moved the torch off my face. She was a nun.

'Are you all right, dear? Can you sleep all right?' she hushed. For a moment I thought I was dead. Then I remembered the ward around me. I nodded.

'Good,' she said, tilting her head to one side and smiling.

I watched her walk round the ward finding other people to wake with her torch.

I spent my days looking at the double doors at the end of the ward, wishing for them to open and frame the shape of someone I knew. My brother and sisters weren't allowed but sometimes my dad came, sometimes my mum. Never together. And it didn't happen every day.

'Are you Angela?'

I looked up to see a tall man hanging over me, large and white. He wore a white coat and was carrying a large wooden box.

'There's nothing to be scared of Angela. I'm a doctor,' he said. He had fair hair and a bushy fair moustache. He smiled at me with his lips but his eyes stayed dead – small, blue eyes like glass marbles. He looked strange to me and I was told never to talk to strange men. I moved away as far as I could on the small bed.

'Don't be frightened,' he said. He put his hand on my arm and showed me his sharp, brown, stained teeth. Was he the wolf that ate little girls, would rip them apart with those sharp teeth? I began to cry and looked to the double doors.

'Mummy, Mummy,' I said but nothing came out of my mouth. I tried to jump out of the bed but the man caught me.

'Where are you going? Just wait here, I'm not going to hurt you.' He lifted up his box to put it on the cupboard. What did he have in there? Hearts of little girls. Little girls like me, whose photos would come on the television and all the grown-ups would shake their heads and say, 'Oh no, not another one missing. When will it stop?'

He opened the box and pulled out a long wire with a rubber ball on the end. I began to scream. He was going to torture me.

But nobody came to me. Nobody tried to rescue me. The nurse and the other patients didn't seem to hear, they didn't seem to care.

'Come on now,' he said, 'I'm not going to hurt you. Just lie still.'

I screamed and waved my arms in the air. He tried to grab for the buttons on my pyjamas but I held on to them with one hand and bashed at him with my other. His face began to get red – his ears began to get red. He held the rubber ball higher. He was going to bash it down on my head, knock me out and take me away.

'I just want to put this on your chest. Come on now, I want to listen to your heart.'

I started to hit out with my legs, too, but they got caught under the blankets. But I kicked and punched the air so nothing could get near me.

'Oh, you stupid girl, you stupid, stupid girl. You're just being silly. You're a silly girl.' His face was red but his eyes stayed glass blue. 'You stupid girl,' he shouted.

I screamed louder and made him start to pack his box away.

'I'll be back,' he shouted into my face. 'I have to do this. I have to listen to your heart. I'll be back when you've calmed down.'

I could hardly breathe. I gulped at the air. I knew he was coming back for me. To take me away. He spoke to the nurse on the way out, the kind nurse, the one I thought liked me. But she looked at me and shook her head. They all wanted me gone.

For the rest of the day I watched the double doors. And I wished and I wished and I wished that my mum or dad would come through the doors before he came back, so I could tell them about the strange man, so they would save me.

But the doors opened and he was there. I was going to die. I lay still on my bed. I was at home in my bedroom playing with my teddy. Smelling milk warming in the kitchen.

'That's better,' I heard. 'See, it doesn't hurt. If only you could have been good before.'

I felt a cold rubber ball on my chest.

'Look,' the voice said, 'if I put this on here, see it makes the pen write here on this paper. Look, see it going up and down – that's your heart making it do that. Here, you have this bit.' A piece of paper was pressed in my hand. 'Have it for being a good girl this time. See, it doesn't hurt.'

But my milk was ready and soon it would be brought to me with two spoonfuls of sugar, just how I liked it. And I'd give Teddy a sip. Then teddy would hug me. And we'd go and play in the yard with a ball.

Then he was gone.

THE POTTY

'Nurse,' I shouted, when I saw her approaching the end of my bed.

'Just a minute,' she said as she walked past.

'Nurse,' I shouted louder. The old woman in the bed next to me said, 'What is it, dear?'

'I need a potty.'

'Oh well, she'll come soon,' she said. She shut her eyes and lay back on her pillow.

'Nurse, can I have a potty?' I yelled. I'd been in hospital long enough to know how to get attention. 'Nurse, nurse, nurse, nurse, NURSE!' I shouted. Within a few seconds the nurse was standing by my bed.

'What is it?' she said with concern.

'I need the potty.'

'Is that what all the noise was about? I thought you were dying.'

'I need the potty. I need to do a number two.' She looked at me, puzzled, then said, 'I'll just get it.' She turned on her heels and walked away, returning a minute later with the silvery metal potty.

'There,' she said, 'no more shouting now.' She placed the potty on the bed, then pulled back the cover. She lifted me up by the arm and sat me on it. 'I'll be back soon, when you've finished.'

'How will you know when I've finished?' I asked.

'I'll be back soon.'

I sat perched on the potty on the bed in full view of everyone on the ward, but I didn't mind, I wasn't shy.

When I finished I called, 'Nurse, I've finished,' but nobody came. As I sat I could feel the warm contents of the potty on my backside. I rested my elbows on my knees and waited. Every time a nurse came into view I called. But no one seemed to hear me. 'Nurse, nurse, nurse, nurse, NURSE!' I shouted, but this time it didn't work. No one came.

I watched the tea woman push her trolley up one side of the ward, handing out cups and saucers of tea to patients, who took them with a nod. I watched her walk back down the other side of the ward. I watched visitors come with little brown paper bags of fruit. I watched them talk and laugh with the patients who'd point to the places on their bodies that hurt. I sat there for a long time. I said the occasional 'Nurse,' more as a whimper than a shout. I felt the contents of the potty go cold against me.

'Right,' the nurse eventually said, startling me with her sudden presence, 'off you get.' I held out my hand for her to help steady me. She held my arm. I stood up but the potty came too. I looked over my shoulder and saw the silvery bowl attached to me like some orang-utan's bottom. I shook my hips, but it didn't move.

'It's stuck,' I said.

'Oh dear,' the nurse said. 'Well, sit down again.' I sat back on the bed. The nurse put one hand on the potty and held my arm with her other. 'Now stand up again.'

I tried to stand, but I couldn't.

'Go on, pull up hard,' she said.

160

'I can't, it's stuck,' I said. 'It's stuck – it's stuck – I told you, you should of come sooner – it's stuck now and it won't come off.' I saw my life flash before me – my school days, my teens, my wedding – all lived with a potty stuck on my bum.

'Just stand up again,' the nurse said. I stood up and the potty came too.

'It's still stuck,' I said with panic. 'It won't come off – I'll always have to have it on – it's your fault.'

'Hold on.' She took my arm and stretched it out until I could grip the bedpost. 'Are you holding tight?' she said.

'It's stuck – I'm going to tell my mum.'

'Now just be quiet and hold on tight.' She then held my back with one hand and the rim of the potty with the other and tried to part us. But I lost balance and began to fall. She caught me and put my hands back on the bedpost.

'Come on now, hold on tight,' she directed. Again she put her hand on my back and pulled at the potty. She screwed up her face as she tugged. Suddenly I heard a loud sucking noise. The potty flew off my bum and into the air with force. The nurse screamed as the potty spun in the air and emptied its contents all over the bed and her. I laughed. It had turned funny.

'You should have come sooner,' I told her.

'Oh, shut up,' she said, picking at the lumps of shit and putting them back in the empty potty.

Chapter 14

They brought my dad home in an ambulance a few days after I'd seen him. They needed the beds.

'What about the blood clot and the shingles?' I said to my mum, who shrugged and said, 'They say it's okay now.'

My dad walked from the ambulance to his bed. He held his leg stiff and straight. He was wearing his slippers.

'Can't get me shoes on,' he explained when I looked down at his feet. It took a while for him to climb the flight of stairs to his bed and he needed support all the way. He looked relieved when he was finally in bed, as if now he could start to get better. He handed my mum some pills.

'They say I have to take them every day. It says on the bottle how many.'

My mum held the bottle and read the label, then placed it with all the other bottles of pills on top of the chest of drawers.

'What are they for?' I asked.

'They're to thin me blood,' my dad said from his bed.

I glanced over at him and saw a thin trickle of blood coming from his nostrils.

'Your nose is bleeding, Dad,' I shouted. My mum looked at him, then hurried from the room.

'I'll get some tissue,' she said as she went.

My dad held the back of his hand up to his nose, then looked at it and casually said, 'Oh, it's bleeding.'

My mum came back and handed him a bundle of toilet

paper. He pressed it up against his nose and rested his head back on the pillow.

'It happened in the hospital,' he said through the tissue. 'They say it's nothing to worry about – just me blood thin now, so sometimes it comes out.'

I sat on the bed and watched the tissue slowly seep with blood. My mum handed him some more and lifted away the soggy red pieces.

'I'll make some tea,' I said.

Chapter 15

THE HAIRDRESSER

'Now Ange, you must sit still so the comb doesn't burn yer head, you hear me,' my mum said. I nodded. 'Keep yer head still, child.'

My mum rubbed Vaseline on the hair then grabbed the hot metal comb from the gas ring, holding it with a tea towel. As it touched my hair I heard a sizzling sound, then smelt burning. My mum pulled the comb through my hair until it cooled, then she put it back on the gas ring to heat it up again. I could feel the heat of the hair gradually warming my scalp and I felt my hair with my hand.

'Oh, Mum, it feels great. Oh, it's great, Mum, just like normal hair!'

My mum continued with the hot comb until it was all straight. My hair smelt singed but hung lank down my back – all frizz gone. But the effect only lasted for a few hours, or maybe a day if you were very careful and didn't move your head too much.

'You must get it cold-straightened, Ange, when you're old enough – like your sisters.'

I looked forward to the day when I'd go with the women of my family to the hairdresser to have my frizz tamed permanently. I was twelve when my mum agreed that now was the time.

The hairdresser's was in Earl's Court. It was called 'Dorothy's'. My mum went there when she first came to this country and had got used to their ways. There was no hairdresser near our home now that understood about hot- and cold-straightening, who understood black people's hair. So we trekked from Highbury to Earl's Court. It was a day out.

The salon was quite smart from the outside. It had a reception area – a desk with flowers on. There were pictures on the walls of women, white women with hair in different styles. But once you got through the beaded curtain into the back, it was a different matter. The once-white walls were yellowed with age and the paint was peeling above the row of wash-basins and line of hooded hair-dryer seats. The room was littered with little trolleys that held creams, pink and blue hair rollers, hair nets and cotton wool. There was a frosted glass window which had ominous bars on the inside and a doorway which led downstairs to another room.

Everyone in the salon was black and female. I had never been in the company of so many black people before. People from the Caribbean like my mum and dad, only 'real' black people with dark brown skin. There were no other black families on the estate where we lived. Another black family came to our church and the girl was in my class at school, but they came from Africa, so my mum said they weren't like us. But at Dorothy's everyone was black. I felt pale in this company, out of place, as white here as I felt black among the pasty-faced English. My mum looked fair and white but her broad African features and Jamaican accent let you know she was among kin.

'Oh, look, you've brought them all today, Mrs Jacobs,' Dorothy of 'Dorothy's' said. She was a tall woman with front teeth that sat on her bottom lip when her mouth was closed and she wore an ill-fitting wig. She felt my plaited pony tail and began pulling it up in the air.

'What's this little one having done?'

'She's having a straighten,' my mum said.

'Oh, you having a straighten, darlin'?' she said smiling at me. 'Come then, darlin', I'll do you meself.' She turned to my sisters. First she inspected Yvonne's hair, pulling it up in the air, then pressing her fingers on the roots. Then she did the same to Patricia. Yvonne smiled but rolled her eyes when Dorothy couldn't see.

'You had a full straighten last time, you just need a bit of a touch-up here, darlin', just the roots,' Dorothy said to Patricia, who smiled politely back. 'You too, darlin',' she said to Yvonne. 'Ahh, but you've both grown. You young ladies now. You like pop music?'

My sisters both grinned, nodded and gave a little embarrassed giggle. I was surprised they were so shy, I thought it was only me who could not think of anything to say and so now hated to say anything in the company of adults.

''Course you do, darlin',' Dorothy went on, 'you're young. Come, I'll get Winifred to touch up yer roots downstairs. Got to make you pretty. You got boyfriends?'

My sisters both giggled again like some goofy twins, but they didn't answer.

'Mrs Jacobs, you havin' the usual?'

'Uh ha,' my mum said, without opening her mouth.

'Same colour?'

My mum looked embarrassed. She giggled too. My mum didn't like us to know she dyed her hair.

Then all three were led away and escorted through the door and down the stairs to the other part of the salon.

I sat in the chair and looked at myself in the mirror. It was the last time I'd see my hair like that. A woman sat next to me with her hair in curlers, flicking through a magazine. A radio sat on the ledge in front of her. It was playing music, pop music.

'Soon come,' Dorothy said, coming up behind me and placing her hands on my shoulders. She walked over to the woman and began taking out her curlers.

167

'How you want it?'

'Same as usual, you know, only a little more height on top.'

They began to talk quickly in thick Caribbean accents and I couldn't understand what they were saying. I listened carefully, caught the occasional word, and smiled when they laughed together. Dorothy pulled at the curlers and placed them in a tray beside her. Then they stopped talking as Dorothy got out a great, fat comb. Her face became tense with concentration. She teased at the hair, smoothing it first with a comb, barely touching it, and then with her hand. She got another comb from her pocket which had a sharp end and she pushed this into the hair and carefully pulled it upwards to give that requested height. The hair stayed where it was put.

'You want lacquer?' Dorothy said as she stood back from her creation.

'Uh ha,' the woman said.

As Dorothy shook the huge can of lacquer, the news came on the radio. She sprayed and the woman began to suck her teeth and tut. Dorothy stopped spraying and listened to the radio, too. The news was saying something about West Indians, how many there were living in this country and how many there would be soon. It talked about a speech someone had given.

'Oh, why don't they leave us alone!' the woman shouted at the radio. Dorothy nodded her head and sucked her teeth.

'Nothing better to do?' she said, changing her nod to a shake of the head. The woman leant over and turned off the radio and Dorothy began spraying her hair again. When Dorothy finished, she got out a mirror and showed the woman the back of her hair. They began talking fast again and the woman patted her hair and smiled. She took off her brown robe and handed it to Dorothy. Then Dorothy turned to me.

'Right darlin', let's get you fix up.' She handed me the brown robe and I put it on. Then she put a towel round my shoulders and tucked it into the neck of the robe, all without looking. She waved goodbye to the woman who had sat in the chair, then she began unplaiting my hair.

'Lovely long hair. You lucky – you have such a high colour and hair like this – your hair is long!' she said. 'You want me cut it?'

'Just a bit,' I said shyly.

She took a pair of scissors out of her pocket and began to comb my hair. The comb got stuck halfway down my head and she could move it no further.

'Oh, your hair in knots,' she said. She put the scissors away and held my head with her hand, then she yanked the comb through my hair. My head went back with a jolt but she pushed it forward again then put the comb in for another stroke. My head got yanked, pushed, pulled and tugged until she finally said, 'That's better.' She took out the scissors again. 'You want it cut to here?' she asked, indicating a place I couldn't see.

'Where?'

She pressed my back somewhere around my shoulders. I nodded.

'Okay, darlin',' she said. I heard the scissors crunching through my hair. After two or three cuts she stood up straight behind me again.

'There,' she said. She picked up a handful of the hair and put it in front of my face. 'All finished. You could stuff a pillow with this,' she said, laughing. I turned and looked at the mass of hair on the floor. It was hard to imagine that I had produced all of it.

'So soft,' she went on. 'You won't miss it though – you want to be modern, don't you darlin'?' I smiled. 'Oh, what a lovely smile. Come, darlin', I'll put on the straightener – I'll do you meself.'

She pulled a trolley towards her and placed the large jar

169

of white cream on the top of it. She pulled on rubber gloves with the intensity of a surgeon before a massive operation. I began to get nervous. She started parting my hair with her fingers and rubbing something on to my head.

'You tell me if it burn you,' she said.

'No, it's fine,' I replied.

She laughed. 'Ahh, darlin', not this, this is only Vaseline. No, tell me if the cream burn you.' She opened her jar and began to smooth the white cream on to my hair. It began to burn me, like something hot nibbling my scalp. Then the pain got more intense. I thought it was going to eat me all up.

'Umm, it stings a bit,' I said, tentatively.

'Stinging you, huh – where, darlin'?' By this time my head was at a barbecue, being roasted on a spit. I pointed at my head. Anywhere. Everywhere.

'Here, darlin'?' I saw her point in the mirror. 'But there's no cream touching your head here, darlin'.' I pointed to another spot.

'Here,' she said, 'I'll put some Vaseline, but there's no cream there.'

My senses told me to run and stick my head in a bath of cold water. Quickly. But I just kept pointing until she said, 'It can't be burnin' you that much. There's no cream on your head.' I could hear agitation rising in her voice. 'I'll do it quick, then we can wash it off. All right, darlin' – just be good. Soon be done.'

I sat and thought of rain, cold rain and wind and that shivery feeling when you come out of the swimming pool. By now someone was using a blowtorch on my head, working their way round slowly. I dug my nails into my thighs. 'Soon finish,' she kept saying. I managed a smile. 'Stop hurting now?' she said.

'Well, no actually . . .' I began, but I could see she wasn't listening. I stopped.

'There, all done,' she said at last. 'Wasn't so bad?' She smiled and gave a laugh. 'Soon have it off and you'll look just like a pop star – who you like, Cliff Richard?'

I didn't answer, I didn't smile, I didn't laugh. I just got up and ran to the sink. Dorothy followed behind me – slowly. I sat with my head back in the sink for some time before she got there.

'Oh, you're in a rush. Where's the fire?' she said, laughing at her joke. She ran the water into the sink. 'You tell me if it's too cold now.'

The shock of the cool water hitting my burning scalp made me give a little yelp.

'Water too hot?' Dorothy asked, removing the stream from my head.

'No, no, it just hurts.'

'Oh, soon come off darlin', not long – good girl.'

My head felt raw and naked as Dorothy began rubbing and kneading it with shampoo, but the fire was out and I began to relax. She wrapped my head in a towel.

'Come darlin', come back to the other chair.'

I wanted to go home now and sit quietly in a corner and wait for the throbbing on my head to go. But Dorothy began pulling out small clumps of my hair, combing out the knots from it, then dexterously rolling the hair round pink, spiky rollers. As the roller approached my scalp she pulled it tight.

'It's very tight,' I said after my third roller, when I felt sure that my head was about to split open.

'It has to be tight darlin' to keep it straight – soon finish.'

She finished with the rollers and led me to a chair under a hair-dryer. She pulled the hood over my head. Then she clicked a dial on the handle of the chair to 'Full' and left. Cold air came out of the hood and its freshness gave me relief. I sighed and sat back in the chair. Then it started to heat up and it got hotter and hotter and hotter. I turned the knob to 'Low' and it began to cool.

I sat under the dryer and every fifteen minutes Dorothy would come and lift the hood, feel one of the rollers and say, 'Still wet!' like she'd discovered some new scientific law. Then she'd turn the dial back to 'Full'. When she was gone I'd click it back to 'Low'.

'Dry now,' Dorothy said after three hours. She led me back to the chair. She pulled the little trolley to her once more and began to unpin the hair rollers. As she took out each roller my hair sprang into curls. When she had taken the last one out she began to comb my hair down. It was shiny. There was no frizz, no fuzz. I started to smile and Dorothy saw me in the mirror. 'You like it?'

I nodded. After all the pain here was my reward. Straight hair. Manageable hair. Not my hair, but hair like my friends – not different.

Dorothy turned and pushed the trolley away from her and I started to get up to go.

'Wait darlin',' she said, catching me by the shoulder, 'I've got to style it yet – can't let you go out with it plain like that.' As I looked at Dorothy, I could see behind her, my mum and sisters sitting waiting for me in the front of the shop. My mum looked as she always did but my sisters were coiffured practically beyond all recognition. Both their hairstyles were the same. Short hair with sideburns that flicked into curls. But their hair had added height. Dorothy obviously specialised in height. The hair was back-combed, stiff and raised. In fact their heads stopped about six inches before their hair did. They looked like the two bewigged ugly sisters from some pantomime. Dorothy pushed me back on the seat.

'Come, I'll style it nice, modern, like yer sisters,' she said.

'No, really, you could leave it now. I like it like this,' I pleaded. Dorothy laughed and put her hand back on my shoulder. She took out a comb. 'Or you want it flick-up like Cilla Black?' she asked.

I nodded, defeated. 'But not too high on top,' I said. Cilla Black sounded all right, anything but like my sisters. As she began flicking hard at the ends of my hair with her deep concentration, I remembered that it was Kathy Kirby who had flick-ups – Cilla Black's hair went under. But it was too late. My hair was straight and shiny to my chin but then there was a roll of hair that sat like a fat sausage round my head. So well formed it looked like a toilet-roll tube was in it. Dorothy got out the mirror and showed it to me from the back. It was no better. She took out the can of hairspray and before I could shout 'No!' she had sprayed it stiff and permanent.

I saw my sisters suppress a laugh as I walked towards them. My mum smiled, thanked Dorothy and paid her.

'You all look nice,' Dorothy smiled. 'You like it?' she asked, looking to my sisters and me. We all nodded.

'See you soon,' my mum said.

As we got away from the salon my sisters began to laugh. They patted at their hair, pulling the height down. And they pointed at me and laughed, clutching their stomachs.

''S not funny,' I said sullenly.

'Why can't she just leave it when it's straightened?' Patricia managed to say.

'Your hair looks nice, child,' my mum said to me, flicking her hand at Patricia to shut her up. My sisters laughed again. Then they pulled open the door of a phone box. They took combs out of their bags and jostled with each other for space, craning their necks to look in the tiny mirror on the wall of the box. They combed at their hair until all height was gone and it looked to their satisfaction, more like their long-haired, peace-loving friends had.

I got in the phone box with them but I couldn't see in the mirror and I hadn't come prepared with a comb.

'What's she done to you?' Yvonne said looking at me. 'I mean, it's nice apart from these flick-ups.' She pulled her comb through my hair and held the flick-up down with her hand. As she lifted her hand away the flick-up sprang back into a roll.

'She said it's like Cilla Black,' I announced, straight-faced. My sisters both looked at each other and laughed so much that it almost made me smile.

THE BARBER

My twelve-year-old brother protested at having to go to the barber, who he had nicknamed 'the butcher'. So my dad decided that he would cut my brother's hair from now on to 'stop all the fuss'.

'Cha, I'll cut it,' he said as he set up two chairs, one facing the other in our small bedroom.

'Have you got an old sheet, Mum?' my dad called. My mum brought him a sheet and several old copies of the *Daily Mirror*. I watched with my brother from the doorway of the room as my dad ceremoniously laid out the newspapers on the floor around the chairs.

'Have you got the scissors, Mum?' my dad called.

My mum came with the scissors, which she was wiping on a tea cloth. 'They're a bit blunt,' she said, 'I've been using them in the kitchen.'

'Come, Johnny,' my dad beckoned, after he had got everything ready.

My brother looked a little apprehensive as he walked towards the chairs. My dad waited for him to sit down, then he carefully wrapped the sheet around him, tying it at the back of his neck. Then he tucked it into the neck of my brother's jumper.

'Just like the barber's,' my dad said, smiling. My dad then sat down opposite John and pulled his chair as close as he could. Then he looked at my brother intently – first this way and then that. He turned my brother's head to the

174

left and then to the right. Then my dad stood up and walked behind him and pushed his head forward. He sat down again in front of my brother. He leaned closely towards him, slowly lifted a small lock of my brother's hair and cut through it with the scissors. He looked at the hair in his fingers for a moment, then threw it on to the paper and grabbed at another small piece from my brother's head.

I stared from the doorway for about ten minutes before I began to get tired of the same scene and went to watch the television instead. After I had watched about three programmes, I realised that my brother and dad had still not emerged. I went and gently opened the door to the room.

'Have you finished yet, Dad?' my brother was saying impatiently.

'No, wait son, I've still got a bit to do at the back here,' my dad said.

My brother shuffled in his seat.

'Hold still a minute – not long now,' my dad said, snipping at the hair. I closed the door.

'Yer dad still cutting?' my mum said as I sat back in front of the television.

I was halfway through my next programme when I heard a commotion. Suddenly my brother sprang into the room with the sheet still tucked round him.

'That's enough, Dad,' he shouted. My dad quickly followed in behind him holding the scissors in the air.

'Just wait, John – I've not quite finished yet,' he pleaded.

'It's been hours, Dad – it's all right now. Just leave it,' my brother screamed. He went to sit down in a chair, but my dad bounced across the room and snipped another bit of hair from his head.

'Get off, Dad!' my brother said, flicking at my dad.

'All right, all right – I'm finished now,' my dad said. 'What a fuss you make.'

My brother pulled the sheet from round his neck and handed it to my dad. My dad took it and went towards the door. Then he stopped and looked back at my brother's hair, frowning. My brother looked at him sullenly.

'You're not cutting any more, Dad,' he warned. My dad sucked his teeth and left the room.

My brother didn't speak but looked at the television with a clenched face. His hair looked shorter but still the same. Not as bad as when he came back from the barber's having accidentally asked for a short back, sides and front, and was dutifully scalped.

'It looks all right,' I said. He looked at me sourly.

'I've been in there hours,' he grumbled to himself.

For about a week after the haircut, my dad would come home from work, stick his head round the door and say 'd'evenin' as usual. Then he would look at my brother and frown a little. He'd come back into the room with the scissors in his hand and pounce on my brother's head and snip off another piece of hair. My brother gave up protesting, he just rolled his eyes, sighed and patted his hair back into place after my dad had finished.

For his next haircut he went to the barber's.

Chapter 16

I heard a howl as I walked into my parents' house.

'God, is that Dad – what's happened?' I said.

'Oh, it's just the shingles. They've been really playing him up,' my mum said, as she kissed me on the cheek.

I took off my coat and sat in the kitchen. I could hear my dad through the ceiling, whimpering like a dog. I wanted to cover my ears.

'Did you give him the pain relief?' I asked.

'Yes, but they're no good.'

'Even the ones I got from the doctor?' I said.

'No good, Ange,' she said with a shake of her head. 'It's paining him a lot, I don't know what to do. He just screams out. I have to tell him to be quiet, in case someone hears. It sounds like I'm killing him or something.' She gave a little laugh and sat down.

'Shall I go up and see him?'

'No – well if you want to, but he's trying to sleep now.'

I didn't argue, I didn't want to go.

'He slept all day yesterday, Ange,' my mum said.

'Really,' I said. I pulled the fruit bowl towards me and began to peel an orange.

'Couldn't wake him hardly,' my mum went on. 'I thought, "funny, he didn't want anything to eat and he didn't drink his cup of tea". He just slept.'

'Mmm,' I said, placing a piece of orange in my mouth.

'Then I found this note,' she said.

'Note?' I said with a full mouth.

'Yes.' My mum looked at me. Her face was grave. 'He took lots of the pills.'

I swallowed the orange hard. 'What do you mean?'

'He took an overdose,' she said.

I stared at her. I must have been frowning.

'He tried to kill himself,' she elaborated. 'Look, look I have the note.' She fumbled about in the pocket of her cardigan, then handed me a small piece of folded paper. I took it, still staring at her. She beckoned me to read it.

Dear Mum

I've taken some pills. I'm sorry to do this to you. I didn't want you to find me like this but I just can't take any more. I'm sorry.

I carefully folded the paper again. A suicide note.

'He took the painkillers – the paracetamol,' she said. 'There weren't as many left in the bottle – there were more before. I was surprised when I went to get them but I didn't say anything, I thought it was me. It was only when I saw the note . . .' She stood up, turned her back to me and began to run water into the sink.

'He's all right now though,' she said.

I looked at my mum's back, which gradually began to blur as tears clouded my eyes and ran down my face. There was a silence. My mum looked round at me and then turned quickly back to the sink and began washing dishes with urgency.

178

Chapter 17

THE STAR

After victory tighten your helmet cords – that was our school motto. In all my days at Highbury Hill High School I never really understood what it meant. Our headmistress would stand in assembly at the beginning of each year and try to explain it to five hundred dumbfounded north London girls.

'When all your work is done girls, when you have made your achievements – it's then you must fight on. You must not sit back on your laurels and think there is no more to be done. There is always more you can do, more you can achieve. So, after exams when you think you can relax, remember the rest of your life lies before you – so tighten your helmet cords for the battles ahead!'

My school was a grammar school and I was one of the élite, as I was told when I first entered its doors. I was one of the children 'lucky' enough to pass my eleven-plus and so find themselves eligible. The school collected girls from all around and assembled them in an imposing Victorian building on the top of the hill overlooking Highbury. The school looked grand amongst the old decaying houses around it. All sorts of girls went there, from 'OK yah' to 'Gordon Bennett'.

It was staffed by grey-haired 'ladies' from another era. They all looked too old to be working but they never seemed to get any older. They were unmarried and had no children and we made up stories about their tragic lives. Lovers lost in the war – never recovering from the shock – resigned to teaching the underprivileged élite – trying to forget the love they'd lost – bitter, twisted. We had to call them all 'Miss'.

They kept us to the 'straight and narrow' with zeal. They made up rules, new ones every day, and made us stick to them with a rigidity the Foreign Legion would have been proud of. We stood up when they entered a room and said good morning or good afternoon no matter how often they came in and out.

My mum and dad thought the school was wonderful – it reminded them of schools in Jamaica.

'They teach you grammar, Ange,' my mum would say. 'You'll never be able to speak properly unless you know grammar – you must know how a sentence is constructed. That's the trouble with the kids round here, they don't know any grammar. You must know how to conjugate a verb and that or you can't speak properly. That's how we were taught in Jamaica. And you all look so nice in your uniform.'

Everything that happened at the school was 'for my own good'. If they'd have nailed me to the roof every lunchtime my mum would have thought there must be 'some good reason to it'.

Our school uniform had to be worn precisely as ordered. It could only be bought from one shop in Victoria, about one hour's bus ride from the school. When you went to the shop they kitted you out with everything you 'must' have. A navy raincoat, a navy blazer, two woollen navy gym slips, two green cotton shirts, one blue and green school-colours striped tie, two pairs of beige knee-length socks, one navy cardigan, one navy purse belt, one navy velour hat with school colours hat band, two green Aertex sports shirts, one navy skirt for gym, one pair of plimsolls, one pair of hockey boots and six pairs of regulation navy knickers.

'What!' my dad screamed when my mum told him how much the uniform had cost them.

'She'll grow into some of it. I got it a bit big,' my mum said.

'Big? Good – we can all wear it,' he said.

'She's got to have it. Everyone has to have it and they look so nice, decent,' my mum pleaded.

'Oh God, so much!' my dad said and held his head in his hands.

The school was divided into houses. Everybody belonged to a house, either Mayo, Newton or Raleigh, and there was competition between them. Music competitions, hours of tuneless recitals on violin, cello, viola, recorder or piano, judged and rewarded. Elocution competitions, with poetry readings, well-pronounced conversations and two-minute monologues on a topic of your choice without drying up. Traditions handed through the decades which were untouched by time or imagination.

Then a new teacher started at our school. She looked young and rumour had it that she'd once worked for the BBC. She was married and drove a green sports car with an open top. Mrs Kromer. She taught music and played the guitar.

Music lessons with her became fun. She made us listen to pop music in the same way we did Bach and Beethoven. She let us make up songs and have impromptu concerts. And she put her arm round me and told me how good I was at music and that I was one of her best. When the annual music competition came round she said, 'Let's have a hootenanny instead.'

A hootenanny, she told a stunned assembly, is an American idea. Like a 'ho-down'. It's a concert, but everybody can get up and do whatever they like. They could sing or dance or recite poetry or juggle – anything. 'Not a competition,' she explained, 'something just for fun that we can all enjoy – teachers *and* pupils.' Auditions were to be held.

I got very excited about the hootenanny. At last a chance to be Julie Andrews. I was going to sing 'Thoroughly Modern Millie' from the film.

'Everything today is thoroughly modern, check your personality,' I sang into the full-length mirror on my mum and dad's wardrobe. I tried it with 1920s flapper actions, like I'd seen on the film. I batted my eyelids, put my hands on my knees and swung them from side to side then held up my palms and made circular movements.

'Everything today makes yesterday slow, better face reality.' I worked out a small charleston routine as I hummed the music. When I'd practised it through once, I started again until I'd got it right.

The auditions were in the music room. None of my friends wanted to do anything. They said it would be, 'too embarrassing. God, how can you, everybody staring at you!'

I sat at the back of the room and watched the act before me. A girl from my year stood with her head down looking at a bit of paper in her hands. 'Hey, little girl,' she began, 'comb your hair, fix your make-up,' she looked up and began to giggle.

'Come on, come on,' Mrs Kromer said gently. 'And could you stop chewing.'

The girl turned her back to the audience and removed her gum. She held it between her thumb and finger as she started singing again.

'Hey, little girl, comb your hair, fix your make-up, soon he will open the door. Don't think because there's a ring on your finger . . .' As the girl sang her head dropped closer and closer to her chest and her voice became barely audible. I leaned forward to hear. When she'd finished she popped her chewing-gum back in her mouth, looked up and smiled.

'That was very nice Carol, very nice, but I think you should sing with your head up, really project your voice like, "Hey, little girl".' Mrs Kromer sang out the words so loudly that it made me jump. Carole looked at her with her mouth open, then began to giggle and chew.

'Well, off you go,' Mrs Kromer said. 'Come back tomorrow and I'll tell you if you've got in.' Mrs Kromer looked tired and talent-weary. 'Is there anyone else?' she said, looking round the room. She saw me. 'Angela, are you going to do something – play your viola?'

'I'm going to sing, Miss,' I said.

'Right, on to the stage,' Mrs Kromer said with a laugh. There was no stage. I walked to the front and began.

I sang, I jumped, I pouted, I danced and I ended with my arms crossed over my body and my knees bent.

'That was lovely, Angela,' Mrs Kromer said, clapping, 'Lovely, I didn't know you could sing – and dance! Well, that was lovely.'

'Thanks, Miss,' I said smiling. I felt like I'd just come off the stage on Sunday night at the London Palladium.

'Have you done it with the music?'

I shook my head.

'Well, we'll need to try it with the piano. I'll accompany you – yes, I'll get the music.'

I grinned.

'Do you like singing, Angela?'

'Yeah, it's what I want to do when I grow up, singing and dancing and that.'

'Well, that was very good.'

She paused, looked round the room, then came up closer to me. She put her head close to mine. 'I tell you what Angela, why don't you come to my house, one day after school for an hour or so, and we can go through it together with the music, then no one will be able to disturb us. You'll be the star of the show.'

I nearly choked with excitement and I nodded my head so vigorously that I began to feel dizzy.

'Next week,' she whispered conspiratorially. 'Next Thursday after school – I'll get the music.'

The wind blew my hair every way and I gulped for breath as I sped through London in Mrs Kromer's car with the top down. She drove fast and made rude gestures to other motorists, then looked at me and grinned. I watched the road where I live go by. I watched the boarded-up shops and old houses with peeling paint and rubbish piled high in the front garden go by. Finsbury Park. Then the landscape began to change. The houses got bigger and there were trees and window boxes with flowers of every colour. Mrs Kromer stopped the car abruptly outside a tall house. It was painted pale green.

'Here we are,' she said.

I patted frantically at my hair so it wouldn't look too frizzy. I followed her up the steps to the front door. She took out a key and pushed the door open for me to walk in first and I stepped into another world. A world from the Ideal Home Exhibition, only someone's real world, not make-believe. The hallway had striped wallpaper and a thick carpet that sprang under your feet.

'Come to the kitchen,' Mrs Kromer said, passing me in the hall. 'I'm sure you'd like a drink – I know I would. I'll fix something for later, too.'

I followed her down a small flight of stairs. Suddenly a room opened up before me, a huge room. It looked bigger than our entire flat. It was bright and sunny, but had the stale air of not being used all day. There was a kitchen area with wooden cupboards. It had a cooker that was halfway up the wall and a fridge so big you could walk into it. I was amazed. There was a dining-table all laid out with a white tablecloth and silver knives and forks with two places set. One for me?

'How do you like my kitchen?' she asked. 'We've just had it done. I'd change a few things if I had it done again, but we're very pleased. Do you like it?'

I nodded.

She unlocked a door and pushed it open to reveal another room. A glass room with stained glass panels like we had at church, only there were flowers on it instead of Jesus. It was hot in the room and full of green plants and flowers. There were cushions on the floor and magazines laid open all round.

'This is the conservatory. Excuse the mess,' she said, picking up a magazine and placing it in a rack. She opened another glass door and a cool breeze skipped into the room. I walked out into the garden. The Ideal Home Exhibition began to feel puny. The garden had a fountain in the middle. Water squirted up out of a fish's mouth and fell in little drops in the pond below. Mrs Kromer caught me staring.

'Just our little decadence,' she said. I didn't know what she meant.

'It's nice, Miss,' I said.

'Where do you live, Angela?' she asked.

'Near the school,' I said.

'In a house near the school – well, that's nice – so you can walk to school every day.'

I nodded and smiled.

'Well, I'll take you back later so you can show me exactly where you live,' she said with a smile. 'Now, I'll get you a drink – you must be thirsty, I know I am – fizzies okay?'

'What?' I said, still wondering how I could get home without her seeing my flats.

'Oh, fizzies – that's what we call lemonade and Coke, 'cause they're fizzy. What do you call them at home?' she asked.

A big treat, I thought to myself. 'Don't know, Miss,' I said. 'Lemonade and Coke, I suppose.'

'Well, is that all right?'

'Yes.'

I watched her walk into the kitchen and open the giant fridge door. A light came on as she did it. She took out two cans and pierced the tops with a can opener. Then she took out a tray of ice and cracked the container so chunks fell into the glass. She poured the drinks, then wiped a cloth round the area and bottom of the glasses. She brought it out to me.

'You'll be all right for a minute? I just want to get something ready for us to eat later – it won't take long.' She went back to the kitchen and began moving skilfully around, picking up pans, opening cupboards, screwing up jars.

'Angela,' she called, after a while. I walked into the kitchen. 'Well, that's the pizza and salad made,' she said. 'You do like pizza?'

I nodded, then said, 'Well, I'm not sure what it is.'

'You've never had it? It's Italian – I'm sure you'll like it. We love it, me and my husband. We first had it in Italy. When I got back I bought a recipe book.' She handed me a book. It had a map of Italy on the front and the words *Italian Cuisine*. I pretended to look through the pages.

'It's very easy once you've made the dough. You'll have to get your mum to try it. I'll write down the recipe for her if you like it. Have you ever been to Italy?'

'No.'

'You look a little Italian. Are you Italian?'

'No,' I answered.

'Where are you from, Angela?'

'I was born in this country,' I said, as I always said to this familiar question.

'Yes, but what about your parents – are they Jewish?'

'No, they come from Jamaica.'

186

'Both of them?'

'Yes.'

'How wonderful – Jamaica, how wonderful. Have you ever been there?'

'No.'

'Do you want to go?'

'Not really.'

'Oh, but it would be wonderful. You must go – how wonderful – so exotic. I've always wanted to go to the Caribbean, all those beaches and sun and rum. Wonderful – you are lucky.'

I'd never looked at it that way before.

'Anyway, we'd better not stand round chatting. Let's get down to some singing – got to make a star of you yet,' she laughed.

I followed her through to another room, equally large and sunny. It had huge sofas and chairs covered in the same floral fabric as the walls and curtains. At one end of the room was a grand piano.

She sat at the piano, laid out the music and began to play. At first I didn't recognise the tune, then she started to hum the melody and I joined in. We went through the song again and again. She nodded me in and nodded all through the playing and said, 'Good,' when I hit the high notes. After an hour it was perfect.

'Let's go and eat,' she said to me, closing the lid of the piano. 'You've worked very hard you deserve your pizza,' she sang playfully.

I sat down at the dining-table and Mrs Kromer handed me a plate with what looked like a ripe pear on it. I stared at it.

'I hope you like avocado, Angela. I had one and it will be too ripe tomorrow and Charles isn't coming in until late tonight, so I thought we could have it.' She sat down opposite me. I waited for her to start as I wasn't sure what I should do with the avocado filled with brown liquid, where the pips should be. She pushed a small spoon into the pear and scooped up some of the liquid then put it in her mouth.

'Ohh, just ripe, just lovely. Try it, Angela.'

She watched me as I scooped up a mouthful. It reminded me of the bar of Palmolive soap we use to wash with at home. I put it in my mouth. The slimy, slippery substance rolled on my tongue and I felt sure it was Palmolive soap. Except the soap had more taste. I tried not to screw my face up too much, but I wanted to spit it out.

Mrs Kromer grinned. 'Do you like it?'

'It's all right,' I lied.

'Well, you finish, I'll get the pizza,' she said, still spooning in her avocado whilst walking to the kitchen.

I thought about putting it in my pocket but that would look like I'd eaten the skin as well. So I took two big spoonfuls and put them in my mouth, then swallowed hard, taking care not to breathe. I rested my spoon back.

'Finished?' Mrs Kromer said, placing a wooden bowl on the table. 'Let me take your plate.'

She returned again with the pizza, all hot and steaming on a large oval plate. It looked enormous. She sat down and began to toss the salad with a wooden spoon and fork, mixing it all up. At home, salads came on a plate – cucumber, tomato and lettuce, side by side. She sliced the pizza.

'Pass your plate, Angela,' she said. I passed the pink floral plate and she put an enormous wedge on it. I began to panic. If it was anything like the avocado, I'd never get through it or be able to fit it in my pocket. I waited for her to start again. She cut herself a small slice and spooned some salad on to the plate beside it. Then she turned the handles of the spoon and fork to me. I tried to pick up the salad but it kept sliding off the spoon. Finally I managed, with great concentration, to keep a piece of lettuce on the tip of the fork and carry it over to my plate. That was enough.

I cut a small piece of the pizza and put it slowly into my mouth. It was delicious. Like cheese on toast, warm and melting. I didn't ask what the coloured bits on it were – I didn't care – it tasted delicious.

'Oh, it's great!' I said involuntarily and a little too surprised. I cut a huge piece and began to chew it with some difficulty because of its size.

'So you want to be an actress?' Mrs Kromer said.

My mouth was too full to answer. I looked at her and nodded.

'Well, I think you stand a very good chance. I think you really have got talent. I could tell that about you from our first class together.' She leaned closer to me. 'You're my special one – I can always spot a special one,' she whispered as if someone else could hear in the room. She leaned back again. 'You show a lot of promise. I think it's an excellent idea.'

Mrs Kromer managed to talk and eat at the same time without any unsightly mouth contents or spraying.

I swallowed hard. 'I'd like to go to RADA,' I said, then took another mouthful.

'Yes, well I think you could be good enough. Your viola playing will help. It's very competitive but you'd stand a good chance, I think. What do your parents say?'

I'd never asked them. It wasn't something we talked about. My brother was the only one that knew of my ambition and he just laughed.

'Not sure,' I said.

'Oh well, there's plenty of time. You should talk it through with them. See where they think is best for you.'

I nodded and folded up the lettuce leaf with my fork so I could get it in my mouth. Mrs Kromer got up and began washing things in the kitchen. I looked around me. I wanted to live like this – eat pizza and drink fizzies every day. Be sophisticated like Mrs Kromer.

'I'll just write the pizza recipe out for your mother, then you can take it home with you,' she said.

The hootenanny came. My mum made a costume of pink lining-fabric satin – a dress with a drop waist. I bought an old hat and pulled it down tight on my head to be like a cloche hat. I put a satin band round it and I borrowed my sister's string of long pearl beads and her white tights.

'What a way you look nice,' my mum said.

'You look good, Anne,' my dad nodded.

The hall was packed with people – pupils, parents and teachers. The stage was lit like a proper stage and there was a curtain. My heart thumped and I sweated from every available pore as I waited in the small side room to go on. Eventually my name was called and a teacher said, 'Go on, it's you.'

I went up on to the stage with everyone clapping. Mrs Kromer smiled and winked at me from the piano then began the music for the introduction. I opened my mouth and my nerves slipped away. I was in a world of my own – I was entertaining.

I looked at the audience and saw my dad sitting, grinning a grin that slit his face in two. He raised a thumb in the air and winked. I did my dance, I jumped and I posed, then it was over. The clapping seemed deafening and went on so long that Mrs Kromer struck up the last chords on the piano and I sang the chorus again. An encore. And as they clapped, I *was* Julie Andrews.

I felt everyone was looking at me as I moved through the crowd at the end of the hootenanny. 'You were the best Angela, honest, I'm not just saying that,' my friends said as they crowded round me. Mrs Kromer came up to me and gave me a hug.

'Wonderful,' she said dramatically, then moved on.

* * *

The night air was cold and quiet as I walked down the hill in between my mum and dad.

'Did you like it then?' I asked.

'Lovely Anne, lovely,' my dad said and patted my shoulder.

'It was very nice Ange, but that other girl was good too, she sang lovely – such a nice song,' my mum said, as she began to hum to herself.

'Did you really think it was good then?'

'Oh yes, Anne,' my dad said. My mum nodded.

'Mrs Kromer thinks I'd be good enough to go to RADA.'

'To where?' my mum said.

'RADA – the Royal Academy of Dramatic Arts – they do acting and that. It's a college, you know, where they teach acting and that.'

'Acting,' my mum said with disdain. 'Acting – waste of time acting.'

'It's not – I really like it. It's what I want to do when I grow up.'

'Cha child, you can't do acting for a living. Acting is a hobby,' she said.

'There are lots of actors. People do it for a living.'

'Who's been putting these ideas in your head? Acting!'

'I like it.'

'So, a job is a job, you don't have to like it. You just have to do it – you have to live. Look at me and yer dad, we do our job to earn money and we do other things that we enjoy.'

'Like what?'

'Like other things – I can't think at the moment – other things.'

'But you can earn lots of money acting – you can get rich.'

'Get rich!' my mum snarled. 'Don't go getting these ideas.'

'Yes, Anne,' my dad began. 'You don't want to get fancy ideas – you'll only be disappointed. Do what you *can* do.'

'I can act and sing – you said I was good,' I said turning to my dad, who shook his head but didn't say anything more.

'You want to go to college, get a good job, then you can think about doing all your fancy things in the evening. People like us don't get famous. Not everyone can be famous,' my mum went on.

'I could try.'

'You'll be disappointed. I had big ideas when I was your age, but you soon grow up. I know!'

'But Mrs Kromer thinks I could—'

'Mrs Kromer thinks! Mrs Kromer this and Mrs Kromer that! Putting ideas in yer head with her big house. She doesn't know! You want to get a steady job. Don't go getting above yourself with big ideas like that. She's not like us. She doesn't know! You want to get a good job. Be a teacher or do typing – you can always work. Learn proper skills. Then you can do all your fancy things in your spare time.'

'But—'

'Cha, I don't want to argue with you, child,' my mum insisted.

I looked at my dad, who was nodding his head in agreement. We walked the rest of the way in silence.

Chapter 18

'How's your dad?' my friend Lynne said as we both dipped pitta bread into guacamole.

The question caused me to miss my mouth and I splattered it down my chin. I leant over and picked up a napkin. 'Not so good,' I said, wiping my face. 'He's got terminal lung cancer and secondary cancer of the brain.'

This conversation had been enough to send other acquaintances at the party off in search of some real small talk about house conveyancing or Czech beer, but Lynne stayed.

'Yes, I heard he was ill. I'm so sorry to hear that. I bet it's tough?' she said.

I looked round the room and gave an embarrassed laugh. She looked me in the eyes.

'How's your Mum coping?'

'It's awful actually,' I said, turning back to the table to cut a piece of cheese.

'Is he in hospital?' she asked.

I began to feel uneasy, emotional. I looked down at my shoes.

'No, he's at home now.'

'Is he comfortable?' She looked at me with a slight frown.

'Well, no actually. He's got shingles and a blood clot as well. He's in a lot of pain and no one seems to care – well, no one except us,' I said with childish belligerence.

I felt a tear in my eye and put a finger up to my tear duct

to try and stop the flow. Lynne gently touched my arm and I turned away from her.

Then she said, 'You should talk to my husband, Alan. He's a GP – he might be able to help.'

She dashed off before I had time to say 'help do what precisely?' The tears were too much for my finger now and I fumbled around in my bag on the floor for a tissue.

'Alan, this is Angela,' Lynne said. I looked up into his face and watched his smile fade. I had wiped mascara all round my eyes and must have looked like a panda.

'Do you want to go somewhere and talk?' he said.

I shrugged and blew my nose into a tissue.

'Let's go to the bedroom,' Lynne said, pulling at my arm.

I walked with my head down through the room full of people, who I was sure were all staring at me.

I sat on the bed and they sat opposite me like a very informal interview. My tissue, which was toilet paper really, was disintegrating into nothing. I concentrated on finding small areas of it that I could stretch open and blow my nose on as I told them about my dad.

'It's just that nobody seems to care,' I said finally. I looked up at them both for the first time. They both nodded at me and smiled.

'You say a district nurse comes?' Alan asked.

'Yes, about once or twice a week.'

'What about the doctor?'

'He only comes if there's an emergency.'

'Yes,' he said, 'yes, it must be terribly hard.'

I gave a little laugh, then there was silence. I was about to make an excuse about needing the toilet when Lynne said to Alan, 'What about Diane, doesn't she deal with this sort of thing?'

Alan's face sparkled. 'Of course, Diane, of course. Brilliant idea, Lynne.' He put his arm round his wife and gave her a squeeze. I watched.

'Diane?' I said.

'Yes, sorry,' Alan said. 'Diane runs a home care hospice service.'

'What's that?'

'Well, it's for people like your dad who are terminally ill at home. She visits them, I think. There's a team. She's a doctor.'

He turned back to Lynne. 'Have you got her phone number?'

'Somewhere,' Lynne said.

'Yes, it's a new thing I think, she's just building it up – it's a brilliant idea. Where does your dad live? It's in our borough, isn't it?'

I nodded.

'Perfect,' he said. 'I'm sure she'll be able to help – I can give her a ring and ask anyway.'

I was a little overwhelmed, but the thought of help or some understanding was sweet to my ears. I smiled. 'That would be great,' I said. 'I mean, it's worth talking to her. Thanks.'

I arrived at work the morning after the party and there was a message on the answerphone.

'My name is Dr Marchant. Alan Abrahams gave me your name, concerning your father. Could you give me a ring back on . . .'

I did not expect to hear from anyone so soon. It was early in the morning and must have been one of the first things either Alan Abrahams or Dr Marchant did. And they did it for me and my dad. I was shocked. I listened to the message again. Was this the charge of the professional class cavalry?

Dr Marchant sounded relieved when I phoned her. She spoke quietly and thoughtfully, finishing every sentence. She asked me questions about my dad, which she took time to phrase with sensitivity. Questions about my dad's

195

drugs, his frame of mind, my mum, her health. She listened without interruption, only saying, 'That must have been distressing for you' or 'Oh dear', to let me know she was still there.

After all her questions she said, 'Is there anything you feel you need to ask me, Angela?'

Then she began to tell me about the service they could offer. The home visits, the drug control, the pain relief. How they could admit my dad to the hospice when they felt it was necessary. How they could give advice on funeral arrangements. And that they would even visit my mum after the death.

It began to sound like a list of delicious food someone was going to prepare for me. I started to salivate.

'The only thing is,' I said, 'my dad doesn't know he's dying of cancer.'

'I see. It's good that you told me. I'll be careful. I presume your mother knows?' she said.

'Yes, but she didn't want to tell my dad – not yet anyway.'

'I see,' she repeated.

'Why haven't I heard of you before?' I said with a laugh, trying to lighten the mood.

'We're quite new. Not a lot of people have used the service yet,' she said in the same tone as she had answered all my other questions. 'I will need the name of your father's GP,' she went on, 'because we'll need to get his or her permission if we're to visit your father.'

'Well, I'm sure he'll give it,' I said.

'You'd be surprised, Angela. Some GPs don't.'

'That's ridiculous – why not?' I said, as a twinge of anxiety gripped my stomach.

'Well, yes, it seems ridiculous to me, but it can happen. Anyway give me the name and I'll get in touch with him, and I'll need your mother's number, too.'

I gave her the information but said, 'Let me talk to my

mum first and tell her you'll be ringing.'

'Of course,' she said. 'I'll have to speak to the doctor first, that may take a day or so, then I'll contact your mum. But let me know if there's any problem.'

I put the phone down. I was light, I hovered inches above the floor. Everything was going to be easier now.

I rang my mum but I could hardly speak, the excitement was choking me. 'I've got great news, Mum,' I said.

'Oh yes,' she said.

I took a breath. 'Where shall I start? Well, this friend of mine's husband is a GP.'

I thought I heard my mum breathe in sharply.

'A doctor,' she said, 'oh yes.' She was impressed. I knew a doctor.

'Yes – anyway, I was telling him about Dad.'

'Oh yes,' she said.

'He said he knew someone that ran a home care hospice service. And Mum, I just spoke to her and it sounds great,' I said. My thoughts ran ahead of my speech. I thought I had explained everything, until my mum said, 'Oh yes, what do they do?'

'Oh right, right,' I said, trying to sound calmer. 'It's great. They can visit Dad.'

'Come here!' she interrupted.

'Yes, they can visit and give Dad pain relief and talk to him and you can ask questions. She's really nice, really easy to talk to.' I lost myself again. 'Where was I? Yes, she can look at the blood-thinning, so you won't have to go to the hospital.'

'That's nice,' my mum said, like she used to when I was young and overexcited, telling her about a school play or trip.

'It's great, really. I'm so pleased. I talked to her for ages and she was so helpful.' Then I changed my tone. 'But it's terrible really, Mum – I mean the only way I found out

197

about her was because I happen to know a GP. I mean what if you don't, how do you cope then?' I said this with disingenuous disgust, because I was pleased with myself. I felt I had made that social climb to a position where I could have influence, get things done. By phone calls or chance conversations with people I knew casually I could make things happen. I felt in control, in charge. 'Is that all right then, Mum?' I said, not pausing for breath.

'What?' she said.

'For her to call you and come and see Dad. Is it all right?'

'Oh yes, Ange,' she said, 'thank you – it was nice of you to think of us.'

The next time I visited my dad, he was sitting up in his chair in the front room. I was surprised to see him there and not in his bed. My first reaction was that he must be feeling better since the hospice service came to see him. But when he looked up at me his stare had a vacancy in it which punched my optimism. He didn't smile, but gave me a feeble, 'Hello, Anne.'

My mum's frenetic tea-making made up for my dad's lack of animation. She was moving for two now.

'How are you – how was . . .? Where was it you went?' she asked.

'Whitby,' I said, still looking at my dad.

'Have a seat, have a seat,' she said, pushing me towards the sofa. 'Whitby – oh, we went there once, didn't we Dad?'

My dad turned his head to look in our direction and frowned.

'You remember, Dad, when we went and watched the boats coming in. It was just you and me, remember?'

My dad lifted his chin in a slow almost imperceptible movement. This was his yes.

'We weren't staying in Whitby, though it's a lovely

place,' my mum went on. 'We were in a camp just outside. I can't remember the name now. Can you remember the name, Dad?'

We both looked at my dad, but he did not respond this time.

'Well, it was nice there, cold though, but I liked it. You wouldn't think I'd like the cold coming from Jamaica, but I can't stand the heat, never could, even when I was there. That's one thing that puts me off going back, that heat.'

My mum screwed up her face. I looked round the room but my eyes kept being drawn to the pathetic man in a red dressing-gown sitting in a chair in the corner. My mum handed me a cup of tea then walked across the room and pulled out the smallest table from the nest of tables.

'Here, put it on this,' she said, wiping off some dust with her hand. 'Would you like a biscuit?'

She held out a plate a little too high for me to see everything that was on it. I took one.

'Oh, you need a plate,' she offered.

'No, no I don't, it's all right,' I said.

My mum placed a mug of tea near my dad, who moved his eyes to look at it.

'Do you want it?' she said to him.

He lifted his hand slightly from the arm of the chair.

'Well, I'll leave it there for when you're ready,' she said, as she turned back to me.

'Did Dr Marchant come?' I asked.

'Yes, yes she came,' my mum said, as she settled down into a chair. She didn't say any more.

'Well, what did she do?' I said, when I realised she wasn't going to elaborate.

'She looked at yer dad then gave him some pills.'

I stared at my mum, waiting to hear more. But she just sipped at her cup of tea and looked off into the distance.

'Did she talk to you and Dad?' I said.

'No, not really, she didn't say much, just looked at yer dad.'

'Was she helpful – I mean, was she a help? Did she tell you what to expect and that. I mean, did she . . .'

My mum twisted in her chair. 'Yes,' she said, but her tone was unimpressed. 'She was all right – quite nice.'

'What did she say?'

'She commented on me daffodils, said how they looked lovely.'

'No, I mean about Dad.' I looked over at my dad and smiled. I felt uncomfortable talking about him while he was sitting there.

'She didn't say much. You know how doctors are.'

'Did she say anything to you, ask how you were or anything?' I could taste my agitation. I couldn't believe that Dr Marchant hadn't come in and taken over, swooped down on my mum and dad and lifted them to a painless place.

'Not really, she was nice though,' my mum said as a reassuring afterthought.

'What did you think, Dad?' I said.

My dad turned his head slowly towards me. His face was cement grey and the lines which were once wrinkles were now gouged grooves.

'What did you think of her?' I asked again.

'All right, Anne,' he said, then turned his head back.

I leant back on the sofa and took a sip of tea. The cavalry charge had left no impression.

I crunched on the biscuit, which sounded like a thunderstorm in the silence of my head. I watched my mum get out of her seat. She went to my dad and gently helped him to lift his mug of tea to his mouth. As he drank it, his eyes closed tight with effort, as if his body was telling him not to bother with nutrients any more. I heard a clock ticking. I'd never heard it before.

My mum sat down again and I looked at her and smiled. 'When did she come?'

'Who?' she said.

'Dr Marchant!'

'Oh, well, she came just after you went away – a couple of weeks ago. She was meant to come back a few days ago, but they rang to say she'd hurt her back and was off sick.'

'You're kidding – really?' I said. 'Didn't anyone else come?'

'No, she's the only doctor, I think. Anyway, they didn't say anything about sending anyone else. They just said she would come when she was better.'

'She hurt her back?' I said.

'Yes, she must have had a fall or something. It's easy done. Sometimes I get backache with yer dad. You can do it lifting or anything. See, humans were never really meant to walk upright. You know monkeys, they stoop. I read it in this book. It's a good book, you might like it. Wait, I'll get it.' She leant over and looked through the glass cabinet where we'd always kept our books. She pulled at a book but several tumbled on to the floor.

'Here,' she said, handing it to me. 'I forget what page – just have a look. It's very interesting. I read it a lot.'

I flicked through the book, not looking at any of the pages.

My mum rested back in her seat and looked at my dad. He began to lift the mug painfully slowly to his mouth. My mum crouched like a cat, poised ready to leap if she saw him in distress. Then she smiled and wiped her nose with her fingers, so her anxiety did not look too obvious.

'You find the page, Ange?' she said.

'Oh, probably,' I said. 'So she didn't come back – Dr Marchant?'

'No, but she will when she's better. I didn't mind her – she didn't ask too many questions, you know. Not like that district nurse.'

'When does she come?' I said, still riffling pages.

'Oh, she doesn't come any more.' The disgust in her voice was emphatic.

I stopped and looked at her. 'She doesn't come – why not?'

'I'm glad she doesn't come,' she said, sitting up higher in her seat. 'I didn't like her. Always asking me me business. Where do I come from – how long have I been here? What's it to do with her? Those sort of people just want to know everything about you. I was pleased when she said she wasn't coming any more.'

'Yes, but why doesn't she come? Did you tell her not to?'

'No, she doesn't come because of that other doctor.'

'Who? Dr Marchant?'

'Yes,' she shouted. 'I told her those people were coming and you know what she said? She said, "I'm not coming if they're coming". I mean, I ask you, it seems childish to me. But she said it just like that. Put out, you know. She said "I'm not coming if those hospice people are coming".'

I could feel the muscles in my body tensing and my mouth becoming dry. Displaced panic. 'But she has to, doesn't she?' I said.

'I don't want her to. Don't like her, always wanting to know me business. Good riddance, that's what I thought. She expected me to beg her to come, I could tell by her face. But she never did anything, just ask a lot of questions. Everything I wanted help with, like bathing yer dad, she'd say she didn't do that. She was useless. I'm glad she's not coming.'

I leant back on the sofa and let the book drop. 'She won't come because Dr Marchant is coming. That's pathetic,' I said under my breath. 'So nobody's been for weeks – not since I've been away?'

'Yvonne called and so did Johnny. We've got on okay. Now yer dad's down here and I don't have to rush up the stairs. It's the stairs I couldn't stand. My knees were beginning to really hurt me.'

'What about when Dad goes back to bed?' I looked across at my dad and smiled, but he seemed oblivious to the conversation that was going on around him.

'He doesn't now – he stays here,' she said. I looked at my dad again and this time saw a fat man squeezed into an armchair, which once gave him plenty of room to move in.

'What, all night?' I said.

'He can't breathe when he lies down, you see, so he stays in the chair.' I must have looked shocked because she said quickly, 'It's all right, I bring blankets and that – you know, his pillows. He's quite happy. I make it nice and cosy. It's all right, isn't it, Dad?'

We both looked at my dad, who was once again trying to lift the mug of tea to his mouth. His hand shook and tea began to trickle down the side of the mug.

'Careful, Dad,' my mum said.

He tipped the mug to his mouth and another thin trickle of tea ran down his chin. His eyes blinked as if he was shaken back to life. Then he coughed. The first came from deep within him like a thunder roll, but the next spluttered tea out of his mouth. My mum was on her feet and she snatched the mug before it spilt its hot contents over him. My dad held his hand to his mouth and coughed in bass tones. In between the coughs, he tried to take a breath. I heard what I thought was the kitchen kettle whistling as it came to the boil, a whistle so sharp that I was not sure which direction it was coming from. Then I realised it was my dad trying to draw in air.

My mum lifted my dad forward and began to pat his back. She moved around him with the certainty of a mother over a baby. The coughing got less, but the search for air became more urgent. He opened his mouth wide and drew in air in great gulps, but they could not satisfy his needs. He gulped again and again and again. He sounded like a donkey. His eyes were wide and wild, full of fright. He began to flail his arms, wanting something to cling to before he drowned. His fingers were spread in alarm.

I moved over to them and put my hand on his shoulder. His body was stiff, hard, and each gulp sent a quake through it. He moved to the edge of the seat, gasping and thrashing, his face scarlet.

My mum let go of my dad and hurried to the window. She fumbled through the net curtains and opened the window as wide as it would go.

'Come, Dad, come over to the window,' she shouted. We both pulled him from the chair, one either side. There was a strong resistance, he wanted to go, but a current wanted to drown him. His donkey growl got louder and he held his hand to his throat. I pulled a chair towards him and pushed him on to it. My mum was patting him, saying, 'Ssch Dad, sschh.'

His face began to tinge blue. I looked to my mum to know what to do. She looked at me, then ran from the room. I wanted to run after her, she left me with this drowning man and no water to pull him from. I put both my hands on his shoulders and shut my eyes. 'Be calm, Dad,' I tried to will through my fingers. My dad grabbed at the net curtain and twisted it in his hand. 'Oh God,' I heard him say. Then I heard the piercing whistle again. The net curtain began to pop off the rail. I prised his hand off it and put my hand in its place. With each gasp he squeezed my hand until I wanted to cry out.

My mum returned. 'I called the ambulance,' she said.

My dad was taking long, rasping breaths, but I could feel his panic fading. He let go of my hand and held his arms clenched by his side. Every breath sounded like a creature from hell.

We sat there, the three of us, forever, until the rasping became familiar, the gulping, an old friend. But the fear of drowning kept us rigid.

There was a knock at the door and within seconds the room had filled with tall men with deep voices. They pushed a green mask on to my dad's face and strapped it there.

'Breathe slowly, sir,' boomed round the room, then they sat my dad in a wheelchair and covered him with a bright crimson blanket that hurt my eyes in the gloom that had become the room. My dad was compliant. He didn't acknowledge anyone, but was just pushed and pulled.

Then my mum was in her coat and standing by the door.

'Take care of it here, Ange. I'll go to the hospital with yer dad. I'll ring you – you could come for me later.'

I nodded and they all left, left the quiet for me.

Chapter 19

THE BOYFRIEND

I was nervous when he asked if he could walk me home. I'd never been asked before. Being asked at all meant that we might start 'going out' together. I was intoxicated with the idea that, at last, after years of waiting, I might finally have a real boyfriend.

We walked all the way back from the youth club instead of getting the bus. We talked and laughed about the people we knew, music we liked, and school. He was nicer on his own, not so 'cock-sure'. I thought I might like him.

I was nervous as I approached home. I went over my kissing experience in my head. I wondered how we'd get round to doing it, how he'd approach me, how he'd hold me, whether I'd make a fool of myself, get it wrong, miss his mouth, trip over his foot. We got to the door and talked, both of us embarrassed and nervous. Then somehow we were kissing.

Then my front door opened and my dad filled the frame.

'What's this?!' he shouted.

We leapt apart. I went to introduce my new hopeful to my dad but he shouted again, in a broad Jamaican accent, 'Who's this? Who are you?' He kept one hand in his trouser pocket and with the other he jabbed and pointed a finger in the air. 'Who are you? What do you want? What you doing?!'

'Dad,' I screamed.

He looked at me and shouted, 'What time do you call this? Coming back with this . . .' For a brief moment words failed him, 'this . . . this ruffian.'

My walk-home friend began to back away from me, and away from the scene.

'Go on, get away!' my dad bellowed. He followed after him, waving his hand in the air, shooing him away.

'Dad!' I screeched. 'Don't!'

My dad turned to me and used the same movement to flick me inside. 'In,' he roared. 'You get . . . cha . . . get!'

Then he turned back to my would-be boyfriend, who was now running away.

'Get out and don't come back,' my dad shouted after him.

He shut the door behind us. Frustration and embarrassment had brought tears to my eyes.

'What did you do that for?' I wailed.

'What were you doing out there?' he said.

'Nothing! He just walked me home.'

'It didn't look like nothing to me, and with a boy like that.'

'Like what, a boy like what?'

My dad looked stunned by my offensive. 'Cha! Don't you give me any of your lip, you hear nuh, no lip.' His accent was getting deeper with anger and he pointed his finger in my face.

'I hate you,' I screamed. I ran into the bathroom and slammed the door behind me. The bathroom was the only place you could be alone and the only door you could lock shut. I sat on the edge of the bath and sobbed. My body pulsed with rage. Why did I have to be born to him? Other dads were nice in their jeans and open-necked shirts. They smiled at boyfriends and even offered them beer. But my dad, in his grey suit trousers from a time gone by – but my dad, he had to shout. He had to shoo them away, he had to embarrass me.

After a few minutes I could hear my dad through the door. 'Anne,' he said more calmly. He rattled the door handle. 'Open up.'

'No, go away. I hate you.'

'Cha, open this door,' he said, more agitated.

'You're so embarrassing,' I shouted.

'Who was that boy anyway? I don't know that boy.'

'Just someone I met at the club.'

'He's not the type for you, Anne.'

'What *type* – what do you know!' I shouted.

'I could see. I could see . . . long hair. He's rough, Anne, rough. I could see.'

'He's not, he's nice.' I began to sob again and couldn't catch my breath. I took short gasps of air.

'Those type of boys, Anne, they rough – they not good. I know, I know!'

'You don't know anything,' I managed to yell.

'I know those boys,' my dad said, raising his voice again. 'I know those boys. Those sort of boys, they only after one thing.' He emphasized every word. 'Only. After. One. Thing. I know, I used to be a boy. You stay away from rough boys like that!'

'You don't know him,' I screamed with full force.

'Cha!' he said, 'don't give me any of your big lip. I know, I know what those boys are like – I'm a man!'

He walked away and I heard him shut the living-room door. I could hear a faint discussion taking place with my mum. I sat on the floor of the bathroom and stayed there all night.

Chapter 20

Back to hospital. Back through casualty. A wait in a wheelchair, then back down the long ward.

This time my dad sat nearer the door, nearer the nurses and junior doctor, who could keep a watch over him. He was propped up in a chair. Lying down on the bed was out of the question now. If he leant too far back his windpipe constricted and he gasped for air. He was permanently attached to an oxygen cylinder by a green mask, which was strapped on his face. It was a large oxygen cylinder held on a frame with a spare waiting underneath. He had to speak through the mask. When he took it off, on the occasions it became uncomfortable, he would breathe unaided, shallow, light breaths. Then he would grab for the mask again and breathe as deeply as his invaded lungs would allow.

All day he sat in his chair breathing the manufactured air. He couldn't read a book, he couldn't concentrate on the words. He didn't look at the paper, he wasn't interested. He didn't listen to the radio, it could not stretch to his seat, and he couldn't stand 'noise in his head'. He just sat, not looking around, not acknowledging other people. He just sat like a statue of a melancholy Buddha.

I visited with my mum. He looked at us and waved his hand to show he'd seen us. I pulled up a seat for my mum, who sat down beside him and I sat in front of him.

'How are you, Dad?' my mum asked. I smiled. My dad moved his hand in the air again. I couldn't think of

211

anything else to say. My mum and I sat looking around the ward at the daily routines and the other visitors, at the flowers, cards, bowls of fruit, the metal bed ends with clip boards on, the dirty beige of the walls, and the white of the well-used bedclothes. I was thankful that here there were distractions. At least here you could sit in silence and still feel you were making an effort.

My dad suddenly stuck out his leg and rubbed his knee. I noticed that his feet were bare. His brown furry slippers were sitting redundant and neat under the bed.

'Don't you want your slippers, Dad?' I said.

He did not answer, but stuck out his leg again and lifted it a little way into the air and pointed at it.

'Get the stool, Ange,' my mum said, 'he wants to put his feet up.'

I took the stool from under the bed and put it down in front of my dad at a distance I thought would be comfortable. My mum had stood up. She gently lifted the outstretched leg on to the stool, then she beckoned me to pick up the other leg and put it on. I put my hand around my dad's calf. It was warm, fat and fleshy, but firm. I lifted it and let it gently down on to the stool. I sat down again. I was now close to my dad's feet. They were swollen, dirty and black on the bottom. And they smelt of decay, of rotting flesh. I looked at the toenails, no longer transparent but opaque and brown, curled and full of dirt, like walnut shells on the ends of his toes. He couldn't have cut them since the last time he could bend in the middle, which was a history ago. I tried to look away, look round the ward, listen to other conversations, but the smell began to make me feel sick.

'Shall I put your slippers on, Dad?' I said. I reached over for the slippers and rested them both on my lap while waiting for his response.

He put his hand up to the mask and pulled it down.

'I can't get them on – they need cutting,' he said.

His voice was different, hoarse and rasping. He had a frog in his throat that I knew no cough could cure. I looked at the slippers and then at his bloated, smelly feet. The one could never go into the other without some surgery.

'I'll cut them, Dad – here – is that all right? Then they'll go on.' I indicated where I could make a cut, which I hoped would enlarge the hole enough. My dad nodded and put the mask back up to his mouth.

'I haven't got any scissors, Ange – have you?' my mum said, leaning towards me. I saw her look at my dad's feet and widen her nostrils as the smell hit her. She leant back quickly, upwind of them.

'I'll ask a nurse – they've always got scissors.'

I borrowed a pair from a young nurse, who anxiously told me to return them when I'd finished. I cut two slits in each slipper so the front would ride up over my dad's enlarged foot. Then I put them on his feet, gently lifting his ankle so they would push right on. My dad nodded his thanks and I looked round the ward to find the nurse, so I could return her property.

She was standing in the middle of the ward. I went to walk over to her, when she said in a loud voice so everyone could hear, 'Is there anyone who wants to go home?' She looked up and down the ward waiting for a response, but everyone seemed to be staring in a stunned silence. 'Well, if anyone wants to go home, they can come and let us know,' she said, looking around her. Then she spotted me half in and half out of my chair. She smiled, she thought my dad was her volunteer. I quickly sat back down and looked away from her stare. I always thought you were sent home from hospital when you were fit. Perhaps once, but now they needed the beds.

I waited until she walked past us and handed her the scissors without looking at her face.

My mum stood up. 'I'm just going to the shop,' she said, 'and I need the toilet.' She mouthed the last word with no sound. I nodded and my dad turned his eyes to her. I watched her walk towards the door. I looked back at my dad and our eyes met.

'All right, Dad,' I smiled.

My dad stayed looking at me. He took a breath, then pulled the mask down from his face. Then he looked at his feet and said, 'I know what's coming next, Anne, and I don't want it – I'm not ready, not yet.' He lifted his head and I could see tears in his eyes. I saw the convulsion of a sob wave through him and the tears running down his face.

I'd never seen my dad cry before, not ever. I wanted to run – get the doctor to stop it – give him something for it. I looked round for my mum.

I put my hand out and laid it on his leg. Then I stood up and put my arm round his shoulder. He put his mask back up to his face and wiped his tears with the back of his hand. I tapped my hand lightly on his shoulder in a 'there, there,' movement, but I said nothing.

By the time my mum got back we were sitting as before, just as she'd left us.

My mum and I left the ward together.

'I'll get a lift with Ange,' my mum said as she kissed my dad goodbye.

I patted his leg and said, 'Bye Dad,' but wanted to kiss him. I wanted to kiss him so badly, but I couldn't. I was held back by an invisible force – habit or embarrassment. I felt the kiss in me, puckering, wanting to come out. But I would have to walk by the oxygen cylinder. What if I slipped and the mask fell from his face? What if he put his cheek to one side and I went to the other? Or I might lean too heavily on his leg to get to him and he'd scream out in pain.

Or he might be shocked at this unusual show of affection from me; he might be sure he was going to die and then really start to sob.

So I patted his leg again and held my hand there a little longer.

'I'll see you soon, Dad,' I said.

We walked through the long corridors of the hospital which all seemed identical to each other. It felt as if you were making no progress on your journey.

'Dad was very upset,' I said to my mum.

She looked at me. A small smile was turning the corners of her mouth.

'He cried,' I said, 'when you went to the toilet.'

'I know he gets upset,' she said. 'I think it might be the drugs, people can get very emotional.'

'Have you told him he's got cancer, Mum?' My mum stopped walking.

'I think so,' she said, then began to walk again.

'What do you mean?' I asked.

'Well, when your dad was bad, after I found the note and everything, I thought I'd better tell him. So I went and I told him that he had cancer.'

'What did Dad say?'

'Well, he was shocked you know. He looked shocked and he started to shake and that. I didn't say anything else in case it upset him more, and he didn't ask anything else, not how I knew, nothing, he didn't say anything, and he hasn't mentioned it again. I haven't said anything, I don't want to upset him. So, I'm not sure if he knows. I told him, I'm sure I told him.'

We walked on further, then she said, 'I think he does know because you know he's always sighing, "Ah this is life" – you know how he always does that – well, after I told him he started saying, "So that was it". He's like that, Ange. He gets bitter – it's why I didn't want to tell him. He just gets bitter, gives up. You don't know him like I do.'

I stopped walking and my mum stopped too. I moved to the side of the corridor and leant against the wall.

'When he cried, he said to me that he knew where he was going next and he didn't want to go yet,' I said in one breath.

'He said that?' my mum said. She looked surprised. 'You see – I think he must know, but he just doesn't talk about it. He's funny like that.'

We walked on and eventually pushed open the door to the outside. The natural bright light made my eyes squint and the smell of air uncontaminated by disinfecting floor cleaner woke me up.

'I think we should get him into the hospice,' I said.

My mum gave a nod. 'Oh yes, I think so too, Ange – it's time, you know – I think it's time. That hospital is too noisy and busy. He needs quiet now.'

'I'll phone Dr Marchant, or whoever, at the hospice service,' I said. 'They'll be able to do that.'

Chapter 21

THE MOVE

'We're moving, Anne,' my dad said, with a triumphant smile.

Moving had been something we were always going to do. When I was little, we were moving to America, so my mum could take part in the 'brain drain'. But we didn't go. When I was in my teens we were moving to Harlow, to start a new life in a new town. But we didn't go. We stayed in the flat in Highbury, settled but waiting to move.

The council occasionally sent us a 'choice' for another council place to move to. The last one we saw was like all the others. We trekked out in my brother's car to find the 'choice' and see if it was better. We were always full of hope. We drove through lovely, leafy places. Places where you'd love to live, with houses that had front and back gardens, window boxes and orderly bins.

'This is nice,' my mum said.

Then we turned a corner on to a bumpy dirt road.

'You sure this is right, Johnny?' my dad asked.

'Yeah, this is right,' my brother sighed. We drove through land that was, up until a few months before, derelict wasteland – far from shops and amenities and far from the houses with the front and back gardens. We bumped down the road until we hit the estate. Half-built, but with the promise of landscaped gardens and shops for your every need.

217

The flat was on the first floor. It was seductively new, clean and painted.

'It might be nice with a bit of carpet,' my dad said cheerily.

'It's got nice central heating. I want central heating – I can't take another winter of cold – it's got nice central heating,' my mum said.

'It's a dump,' my brother said.

'Come here!' I shouted. We all congregated in one of the back bedrooms. It was large and airy with a huge picture window. And out of the window, about twenty feet away, a motorway flyover swung round a bend towards us. You could see the whites of the drivers' eyes. A car-spotter's paradise.

'Oh,' my dad said, 'it's a bit close.'

'No, it's not right,' my mum said. 'Why can't they give us something on a road with other people?'

'It *is* on a road, Mum,' I laughed, but no one else did.

'Look at this dump – who's goin' to want to live out here?' my brother said.

'Nobody *wants* to – they have to.'

Since that last 'choice', the talk of moving had gone away for a while. The need for more room became less urgent with time.

Patricia got married when she was eighteen, and went to live in Cardiff with her new husband and their little baby. She had a wedding at a registry office and a reception at her new in-laws' house. We were far outnumbered by his huge extended family, who all turned up in their everyday working clothes, as weddings were no big deal to them. My sister tried to conceal her five-month pregnancy by wearing a black all-in-one pants suit.

'Black, you're not getting married in black, nuh.' My mum was horrified, more by the suit than the pregnancy.

'Might as well,' my sister moaned. 'Why not – why not black? Might as well be black – who says it has to be white

218

– at least it's not hypocritical if it's black.'

But she wore a yellow feather boa on the day, to brighten the outfit.

Yvonne trained to become a nurse.

'The batch a nurse!' my brother said to me. 'I don't believe it.'

The thought of my eldest sister attending to sick people's every need was unimaginable. Frightening.

'I hope I'm never one of your patients,' I told her.

'Oh, shut your mouth,' she said. When she became a trained nurse, she went to live in New Zealand. It was the furthest away she could get.

'The fallout from the bombs can't get you there,' she said.

'What bombs?' I asked.

'Nuclear bombs – the wind won't blow on to New Zealand, so you're safe there.'

'But what if they bomb New Zealand?'

'Oh, shut up,' she said.

My brother John travelled. He travelled all round Europe by himself. Then to Africa on a huge truck with others. Then he went to live on a kibbutz in Israel. He moved all the time.

I went to art college and for the first year I stayed at home. I still dreamed of moving, but I wanted to leave home and get a flat of my own.

Then my parents finally had an offer they wouldn't refuse.

'It's a house, Anne – three bedrooms and a big kitchen – first house we've been offered. I think you'll like it, Anne. Get your own room at last, ehh,' my dad laughed, excited.

'Has it got a garden?' I asked.

'Yes, a little one, but there's the river as well.'

'A river – what, the Thames?'

'No, a little river out the front, with boats though.'

I couldn't imagine this place in London.

'When did you go and see it?'

'When you were at college – the other day,' he said.

'Why didn't you tell me?'

'We didn't want to get your hopes up. We didn't want you disappointed again. I think you'll like it though, Anne.'

'Well, it's not up to me,' I said, laying the groundwork for my leaving home. 'I mean, if you like it, you're the ones that are going to live there.'

'But it's your home too, Anne,' my dad reminded me.

'Yeah – but I may not be there long!'

'What do you mean?' my dad said.

My mum came into the room, grinning with the thought of the news of moving.

'You hear, Ange?' she said. 'It's a nice place – what do you think about it?'

'I was just saying that I may not be there long.'

'How do you mean?' my mum repeated. They both stared at me.

'Well, you know, I might get a place of my own.'

'What?' my dad said incredulously.

'Well, you know, I've been talking with some friends – we might get a flat.'

'What flat – what friends?' my mum snapped.

'Friends at college!' I said indignantly.

My mum tutted and looked away from me.

'You got a place then?' my dad said.

'No, it's nothing definite,' I said, looking at my mum, trying to get her to look at me. 'You always said I should get a place of my own.' I remembered the time she said, 'You'll meet a better class of person at college – you need to find somewhere nice to live.'

There was silence.

'I mean, I can't live here for ever,' I added.

'Yes, but that was before – before we got offered this

nice place. You don't need to go anywhere now,' my mum said.

'Yeah, but I can't live with you for ever.'

There was another silence.

'How you going to pay for a flat? They're expensive, you know,' my mum said.

'I know, they said at college they can change my grant to one for living away from home. All they have to say is that it's better if . . .' I stopped myself.

'Better if what?' my mum said.

'They just say it's better for me if I live away from home.'

'Why?'

'Well . . . they just say I'd be better off.'

'So, what, you tell them me and yer dad treat you bad?'

'No – no. It's not like that.'

'What lies did you tell them then!'

'I just said I wanted to live on my own,' I insisted.

'So, what they think of us now – they think we treat you bad?'

'No,' I shouted. 'It's not like that!'

There was silence.

'Well, I suppose you're growing up,' my dad said, but my mum just shrugged.

'It's nothing definite anyway,' I said.

'Well, everyone gone,' my mum sighed.

'You've got Willie,' I said. My dad smiled. 'Anyway, it's not definite yet.'

'No, no, Anne, it's nothing definite, is it?' my dad said.

I shook my head.

'Anyway, once you've seen the new place, you might change your mind,' my mum added.

I went to see the new house with my mum and dad the next day. I drove them in my old beaten-up car. We drove through lovely, leafy places. Places where you'd love to live, that had houses with front and back gardens. And then we turned off on to another dirt track, along a bumpy road. We seemed to drive through a building site for ever. Then we reached a part where the houses were finished. They were neat little houses. Standing together, they looked like a little model village you might find in a park. As I got out of the car I imagined that when I stood up straight I'd be taller than them.

Inside the house, everything was brand new. The floorboards were almost white and the whole place smelt of sawdust and 'just done'. It was small inside, but bigger than our flat. The ceiling seemed to be very close to my head – I felt like a giant. In every room the paintwork shone. It was empty and uncluttered, and the bathroom was clean and had a wash-basin.

'No more washing in the kitchen sink, ehh, Anne?' my dad said. He followed me around with a grin on his face, like he'd just made the house all by himself and wanted to know what I thought. 'You like it, Anne?'

'It's great, Dad, really nice,' I said.

'Yer mum and me thought you'd like it. It's the sort of place you not ashamed to bring people back to. See the river?'

Out of the front window, through a gate you could see a river and beyond, a field. If you half-closed your eyes you could imagine you weren't in London, but in some idyllic Berkshire new town.

My mum went round with a tape measure, measuring up windows then standing, thinking hard with her hand on her chin and her eyes half-closed.

'You can have this room, Ange, and yer dad and me will have this one.' She showed me into the rooms, walking into the middle of them and turning round.

For a moment I was excited. A room to start from new. Not lived in before. A chance to find out what my taste was like. No boxes piled high with Yvonne and Patricia's junk, which they were going to 'collect soon'. No 'make-do' carpet and curtains. Everything would be just as I wanted. Except I wanted to get away.

'This little room,' my mum explained, opening a door to the tiny third bedroom, 'this room I'm saving for Johnny when he comes back. I'll put all his stuff in and make it nice so we can use it for anyone who comes to stay until then.'

'Is he coming back then?'

'He has to come back sometime,' my mum said.

'What about Yvonne?'

My mum pretended not to hear. 'Have you seen the kitchen?' she said. 'I've always wanted a kitchen you can sit in. And the bathroom – like Dad say, no more washing in the kitchen sink, ehh?' she laughed.

Suddenly there was a huge, thundering noise, which rattled the house and shook the boards under my feet.

'What's that?' I screamed above the din. I looked at my mum and dad, then out of the window. Beyond the wall at the bottom of the garden a train thundered by.

'It's a train,' my dad said, as if I hadn't guessed. The noise died down and I saw the lines of track passing just yards from the house. 'It's not a busy line. Yer mum and me counted how many trains go past in an hour. It's not bad when you get used to it. And you soon get used to it. Don't you, Mum?'

'I almost don't notice now and I've only been a couple of times. It's not all the time. It just come, then go, and it's nice and peaceful. Quite interesting really, seeing all the signals go, and the trains,' my mum commented.

'What line is it – where do the trains go?'

'Not sure,' my dad said, 'but it's a little line – not many trains.'

I looked at the junction of lines, and the signal boxes and signals, and hoped they were right.

★ ★ ★

223

On the day of the move Willie didn't want to go, she wouldn't get in her box.

'I can't get her in the box – she won't come,' my dad said with panic. He stood in the hallway of the empty flat. His words echoed round the walls. The place looked dirty and on the floor were bits of old paper and rubbish that he was trying to clear into a black plastic bag. He began to pick pieces of the rubbish up from the floor but more seemed to appear to take its place. It hadn't taken the removal men long to take all our years of belongings out and pack a lifetime into the back of a van. Only Willie was left.

'We'll have to get the RSPCA,' my dad said.

'Don't be daft,' I replied.

'Well, what else we going to do?' he shouted. 'She won't come – she snarling – she vicious. She's not like other cats – she like a wild cat. I don't know what's wrong with her – she want to stay. The only thing I can think is to get them to come and get her.'

'They won't come out to get her. What do we say, "Can you come and put our pet cat into a box please?" They'd think we were mad.'

'Well, leave her then!' he said, with a wave of his hand. 'If she doesn't want to come with us, she can stay. Let her get on with it. She doesn't want to come with us – leave her – I don't care – just leave her.' My dad shouted and mumbled to himself as he grabbed rubbish from the floor. 'No one wants to come to the nice place. You try and do your best, but what for? Leave her – leave her!' he went on.

I picked the box up off the floor.

'Where is she?' I asked my dad.

'Leave her, Anne, leave her. I'm not bothered – leave her,' he shouted.

I walked into the empty bedroom. Willie was sitting neat and pretty on the window sill, looking out as she always did. She looked so harmless, so innocent. I went up to her and she stretched up on me and I picked her up and held her on my shoulder. I slowly walked across to the box. As she saw it, she jumped off me. I tried to hold her but she hissed and caught the back of my hand with her claws. I took my leather gloves from the pocket of my coat and put them on. Then I pulled the sleeves down on my jacket. I grabbed her by the neck. She began to hiss and snarl and lash out at me with her claws. We fought and got tangled up in the net curtains, but I lifted her and pushed her down into the box. I closed the lid quickly and held it with both hands. Her snarling soon became a whimper, a pathetic little noise that made me feel like a beast.

'It's all right, Willie,' I said, as I put my gloves away.

'You got her?' my dad said, surprised. I tried to look composed.

'Yeah, she just came – she's all right,' I lied.

'Oh, good Anne – I don't know what we'll do when you not here,' my dad said.

'Shall we go then?' I said, pretending not to hear.

'Yeah, I'm leaving this rubbish – there so much – how's there so much rubbish? Let them clear it. Be pleased to leave this place, eh Anne? Good riddance,' my dad said.

We walked on to the balcony and my dad unceremoniously slammed the door shut and walked off. But I looked back.

Chapter 22

'I'm afraid Dr Marchant's still away on sick leave but is there any way I can help? I'm Sister Vaughan, I work with Dr Marchant,' the voice said. It was softly spoken and lilting with concern.

'Dr Marchant visited my dad, Mr Jacobs. She gave my mum this number.'

'Yes – Mr Jacobs – are you his daughter?'

'Yes, I am.'

'How is your father?'

'Well, that's what I'm ringing about – obviously, I suppose,' I laughed. 'It's just that we feel my dad should be admitted to the hospice now. Dr Marchant said she would arrange that, so I was wondering what we do next.'

'Ah, right,' she said. I could hear paper being rustled in the background. 'Well, what I can do is fill out some forms with your dad and then get him admitted.'

I felt a sudden panic. My dad would have to know that I wanted to put him in a hospice. He'd think I'd given up on him, that I now wanted him to die. He said he didn't want to go, not yet. Would he want to be somewhere where all that was expected of him was that he leave this life? I saw him looking at me, as he realized he was being sent to die. A final betrayal.

'Does he have to know?' I asked.

'We like to get the patient to sign the form if possible so they know what's happening,' she said.

'It's just that,' I laughed again, 'it's just that, I'm not

sure that he knows he's going to die. He's very upset you see – I don't . . .' my voice trailed off. How can you explain your family conventions – the secrecies, the codes, the quirks, to someone who's never lived them?

'I could talk to your dad. We could explain. A hospice is not only for the dying. Lots of people go in and out,' she said, with a calmness that quieted my fear.

'Well, let's do it then. When can you go to see him? He's in hospital at the moment,' I said.

The voice went quiet on the end of the phone, then said, 'Oh, he's in hospital. Well, I'm afraid I would have to wait until he came out.'

'It's the local hospital,' I said. 'It's nearer to you than my parents' house.'

'No, you don't understand,' she went on. 'The hospital won't allow us to visit patients in their care.'

'But it's the same health authority.'

'Yes, I know it seems silly but we're not allowed to visit people in the hospitals. It's something we're trying to overcome, but for the moment I'm afraid I can't go and see him there. I'll have to wait until he comes out. Sorry.'

'But I was hoping he could go straight to the hospice – he's very ill,' I pleaded.

'Yes, well, the thing is to let him come out of the hospital, then I'll come round, fill in the forms and get him straight into the hospice. It will be quick. But I'm afraid it's the only way I can do it.'

I didn't respond.

'Dr Marchant would have had to do the same, Ms Jacobs, but don't worry – there's no great admission procedure like in hospital casualty. It will be very quick.'

I trusted the voice again. It was calm and soothing. I wanted my dad to hear this voice. This voice would make it all right. All I had to do was bring my dad home from that noisy hospital.

'Is it the only way?' I said finally.

228

'Yes,' she said.

My mum was not sure about my dad coming home.

'He didn't look well enough to come out to me,' she said.

'But it's the only way we can get him into the hospice.'

'Well,' my mum looked resigned, 'well, I suppose so – they need the beds anyway,' she said.

My dad was not sure about leaving the hospital. 'I can't breathe without this oxygen,' he muttered.

'I know, Dad,' I reassured him. 'I've got it all sorted out. The doctor gave me a prescription for two cylinders of oxygen and the man was great at the shop. He said he'd come and replace them any time. So you don't have to worry about that. It's there waiting.'

He looked at me. 'You sure it's the best thing to do, Anne?'

'Yes, Dad,' I said, with the necessary confidence, which wilted in my stomach as I expressed it.

My mum and I waited by the door as we saw the ambulance pull up in front of the house. Everything was ready. The oxygen cylinder was waiting and the pillows were plumped up and pushed into shape on the chair. I had phoned the hospice service and told them the day my dad was coming home. Sister Vaughan told me to ring when he was there and she would come as soon as she could with the forms. I'd organized it – I'd sorted everything out with the precision of the German railways.

The wheelchair ramp lowered and a man in a uniform pushed my dad toward the house. It was like having a parcel delivered. Then I saw my dad. It was hard to tell whether he was dead or alive. He didn't look at us, or say hello, or smile. He was just wheeled in like a statue, with sunken eye sockets to give the illusion of eyes and a face of grey marble that had been carefully chipped away at for every groove.

'Where shall I put him?' the ambulance person asked. My mum pointed to the door of the front room. Then we parted to allow the chair through. I stood in the trail left behind them, not wanting to move.

A man came out of the back of the ambulance and walked up to my mum. 'I was told to give you these,' he said, handing my mum a white carrier bag.

My mum smiled and thanked him, then said, 'What's in here?'

'His medications and that,' the man said. He turned his back and went to the ambulance. My mum opened the bag and looked in.

'Oh my God!' she said. She looked back for the man, but he'd disappeared. She put her hand in the bag and pulled out a brown labelless bottle. 'What's this for?'

I went to take the bottle, but the other ambulance person appeared in the doorway of the room.

'I've put him in the chair,' he said. We went into the room and saw the fat, grey figure sitting small in the corner attached to an oxygen cylinder.

My mum held the bag out. 'Do you know what all this is for?' she said to the man with unusual assertiveness.

'Oh, no madam, if you've got any problems like that I should contact the hospital or the doctor, only we weren't given any instructions, except about the oxygen.'

'Oh, okay,' my mum said.

She saw the man to the door and shut it behind him.

The house was quiet again. My dad looked vacant but peaceful in his chair. He rhythmically inhaled his air and shut his eyes. I wasn't sure if he knew we were there, or where he was.

My mum looked in the bag again as she handed me the bottle of pills.

'What's this?' she said, lifting out a piece of funnel-shaped plastic. 'What's it for?' Then she pulled out several more boxes and jars, which rattled with pills and potions. She put them down one by one on the coffee table, then turned them round looking for clues for dosage or instructions, but there were none on them. She put her hand in the empty bag and felt around.

'Nothing, Ange, there's nothing in there to tell us what to do. I don't know what to give him – I might get it wrong, make him more ill. Cha, I don't understand – there's nothing. They can't do that.' She looked at me with a frown of total bewilderment. She was scared.

'I'll phone the hospice service,' I said. 'It'll be all right, don't worry.'

'Sister Vaughan won't be in again until Monday.'

'What!' I screamed involuntarily at the voice on the other end of the phone, 'that can't be right. It's Friday, she told me to ring as soon as I got my dad home.' It crossed my mind that I may not have been making sense to this stranger's voice, but I didn't care. 'It's an emergency,' I said. 'Is there no way I can get hold of her or could you help?'

'Who am I speaking to?' the voice said.

'Jacobs – the name's Jacobs. Is there anyone who can help?'

'I'm afraid, Ms Jacobs, that Sister Vaughan won't be in until Monday.'

'I know that!' I shouted. 'It's an emergency – she said to ring – that she'd come straight away. Monday is no good.'

'I am sorry, Ms Jacobs, I realize this is a difficult time, but there's nothing I can do. I'm just the secretary. I can take a message and tell Sister Vaughan the minute she gets in but I'm afraid that won't be until Monday.'

I was beginning to recognize the technique for 'dealing with the terminally sick and their families'. They all had it, probably all went on the same course together – calm,

231

sensitive, caring and reassuring always. But today I needed effective.

'Isn't there anyone else?' I said.

'At the moment, Ms Jacobs, we're short-staffed because our doctor is off on sick leave with a bad back. It's unfortunate, but you'll have to wait until . . .'

I slammed down the receiver.

'What did they say?' my mum said, as she walked towards me.

I didn't tell her. I didn't want to lift my head and show her the tears of anger and frustration in my eyes. I didn't want to tell her that the people I had sent to them, the people I had pulled my dad from hospital for, the people I had trusted with my dad's death, couldn't come and see him until Monday – two days away.

'What did they say?' she repeated.

'They can't come until Monday – she's not there,' I said. I didn't look at her, I stared at the phone.

'Monday,' she said. 'Monday's no good. What about all the medicine? Monday's no good! Your dad's very bad, he doesn't seem to know where he is. They shouldn't have let him out. Monday's no good!'

I could hear the panic rising in her voice.

'I know that,' I snapped at her, to shut her up. I walked into the kitchen and sat down at the table. I looked at the cooker and thought how it needed cleaning around the knobs. Little bits of old sauce were clinging. I shut my eyes.

I could hear my mum dialling a number on the phone. I tried to breathe steadily so I could hear her more clearly.

'Hello. I wonder if I can talk to the doctor? . . . Mrs Jacobs . . . no, Jacobs . . . When will he be free? . . . It's about my husband . . . yes . . . well, I'd like to speak to the doctor . . . umm, it's just that he's just come from hospital and I've been given lots of drugs for him, but I don't know what they're for and I . . . well, I wondered if he could visit

. . . yes . . . what, ring me back . . . oh . . . oh, good, thank you . . . Good afternoon, Doctor. How are you? Yes, I'm ringing about my husband. He's been in hospital and he's just come home and they've given me lots of pills and things, but I'm not sure what they're for . . . No, no instructions . . . yes, there are names on some, but I wondered . . . No, they were sent from the hospital . . . in an ambulance about half an hour ago . . . He seems all right, just sitting in his chair, though he isn't . . . Yes, we got the oxygen . . . It's just that I don't know when to give the pills, I thought you might be able to . . . oh . . . oh, yes . . . oh, yes . . . I see . . . oh, right . . . I see . . . right . . . well, if he gets worse, yes, but . . . oh, yes . . . right, well, thank you, Doctor.'

She put down the phone and came into the kitchen.

'That doctor,' she said, spitting out every word, 'he's useless – they're all useless – they don't care. They only care if you're paying them.'

'What did he say?'

'Says I'm to ring if he gets worse, then he'll come. He's useless. Says if Dad's all right now then there's no point him coming. He didn't seem to want to know about this pills problem because he didn't give them to him. Says I should ask the hospital. But I need someone to look at them, tell me what to do. I could kill him with all these pills. Useless, all these people. They don't care about us. Says if he gets worse he'll come. How much worse – have you seen him, Ange? He's not all there – he's not right.'

We walked into the room and stood in front of my dad. His eyes were open, but they were staring at some place I couldn't see.

'Dad,' I said. He did not respond, but kept breathing deeply on his air.

'See what I mean, Ange? He's not there,' my mum said.

I waved my hand in front of his eyes, but he did not blink or look at me.

'See?' my mum said. 'What are we supposed to do now?'

We looked at each other and a lifetime passed between us. Mother and baby, mother and daughter, daughter and mum, women. Alone and lonely together, with a dying man.

'We'll have to send him back to the hospital,' my mum said into the vibrating silence.

'I know,' I said.

Chapter 23

THE FAMILY TIE

'So you've been away then, Dad?' I said.

'Who said?' he replied abruptly.

'Mum – she said you'd been away for a few days – where'd you go?'

My dad going away somewhere by himself was, well, unheard of in the history of our family. My dad went to work and came home and he went on holiday with us or my mum. Occasionally he might spend an evening away from home 'playing cards', but generally he was always there.

He looked a little reluctant to give any details of his trip, but I persisted.

'Where did you go?'

'Just to the Midlands, up near Leicester.' He sat down and lit a cigarette. He pulled the ashtray towards himself, then rested his head on his hand and looked into the distance.

'Why did you go, Dad, was it work or something?'

'Nah,' he said. There was silence. I sighed.

'Well, what did you go for?'

My dad looked at me with a half smile and said, 'You ask a lot of questions.'

'I'm only trying to make conversation,' I said.

'Well, if you must know, I went to see me brother.'

'Your brother!' I said. I was startled and said it too

235

loudly. 'I didn't know you had a brother.'

'Of course,' my dad said. He flicked ash from his cigarette. 'Of course, you know me brother.'

'I don't, Dad. Honest, you have never told me you've got a brother. I don't remember you saying you have a brother.' I stared wide-eyed, waiting for more.

'Well, go on,' I eventually had to say.

'I got a phone call, the other day, said he wanted to see me – Louis, me brother – but he didn't know where I live.'

'Really? How did you get a phone call then – who from?'

'It was the Red Cross or Samaritans, I'm not sure. One of them do-gooding places. They gave me his address and phone number.'

'Did you know he was in this country?' I asked.

'Yes, but we'd lost touch long, long, long ago,' he waved his hands in the air to demonstrate how long ago it was.

'So you went to see him. God! What was it like?'

'Well, you know he's me twin.'

'Your twin?' I shouted.

'Cha, keep your voice down,' he said. 'Yes, you know we're identical twins.' He puffed on his cigarette as if he'd just told me the time.

I paused for breath, then laughed. I was twenty-five years old and for the first time I was hearing that my dad was an identical twin, that somewhere on this earth was someone who looked the same as my dad, someone who had grown up with him, in his image. A parallel being.

My dad looked at me. 'What's so funny?' he said.

'I never knew you were an identical twin, Dad. I never knew that – you never told me.'

'Oh, I never told you?' he said. 'Well, you know now.' He smiled.

'How was he then? God, I can't believe this,' I said. 'And he lives in this country, but we've never seen him?'

'We lost touch, but, you see, he was ill so that's why they contact me. He wanted to see me, so I went,' he said.

'He's ill – what's wrong with him?'

My dad curled his mouth up and said, 'Lung cancer,' quietly. He looked away from me and stubbed out his cigarette. He stood up and went to the sink.

'D'you want a cup of tea, Anne?'

'Is he in hospital?'

'He was,' he said.

'What, is he home now?' I asked.

'No, Anne – he died.'

I sat back in my chair. This conversation was brief, but condensed. First, I find I have an uncle in this country. Second, that he's my dad's identical twin and lastly, that he is dead. I had learnt more about my dad in those few minutes than in most of the years that got me to that point.

'I'm sorry to hear that, Dad,' I said.

'Yes, but it was the best thing. He was real bad, thin, so thin. I thought he wouldn't have long.'

I imagined my dad visiting the hospital seeing the image of himself lying thin and dying on a bed. That would affect you – that would change you.

'It must have been awful, Dad,' I said, feeling a tender moment.

'Well, it was a bit upsetting,' he said loudly, filling the kettle, 'but I'm all right now.'

'It was only last week!'

'I know, Anne, but I feel all right now. You can't let these things bother you.'

Chapter 24

I rang my mum the next morning but I couldn't get any reply. So I rang the hospital to see how my dad was.

'Miss Jacobs,' the nurse said, 'yes, your mother's here with him now. Would you like to speak to her?'

I could hear raised voices in the background as the nurse put down the receiver to go and get my mum. It sounded noisy there, like a railway station with a paperseller rising out above the din every so often.

'Hello,' my mum said.

'Hi, Mum, it's me – what's the commotion there?'

'Oh, Ange,' she said, 'it's your dad, they called me to come – he's bad, he keeps crying out. Can you hear?'

She stayed unnecessarily quiet so I could hear the muffled screams clearly. 'What's happening to him? What are they doing to him?'

'Nothing now. They had to put a thing in his private parts so he can pee, but they're not doing anything now. He's in pain and he's just screaming out. It's embarrassing really. Can you come, Ange?'

I drove into a parking space in the hospital grounds and turned off the engine. For a moment I sat and stared through the windscreen at the building I was about to enter. In that building were experiences waiting to test me. There was pain there – not physical, not for me, but pain that you can't see coming, that smacks you inside and pulls and rips at you. No aspirin or plaster can help. I looked at the building and cursed my selfishness. I didn't want to go in. I didn't want to go through it. I didn't want the experience. Like a child waiting outside the dentist, anything would have been better. Let the dentist pull out all my teeth now.

As I walked up the ward I could see my mum sitting in the chair by my dad. She had her coat on, still buttoned up, but she looked like she'd been there a long time. My dad was in his usual place in a pale green hospital nightshirt. He was strapped to his cylinder and sat forward in his chair with his hands resting on his knees. He stared down at the floor. The jerky movement of his inhalations tipped his head back and forward. But he was quiet. My mum went to stand up to give me her seat, but I pulled out the stool from under the bed and sat opposite my dad, just as we'd been sitting a few days ago.

'How is he?' I asked.

'Oh, he's all right. He's quiet now.'

I looked at my dad and smiled, but he didn't see me, he just stared at his space on the floor.

'All right, Dad?' I said out of courtesy, but he did not give a response. I leant against the bed and looked round the familiar ward. I smiled at my mum. 'How long have you—' Suddenly my dad pulled at the mask on his face and let out a roar, a roar with power and force that put fear into me. I was startled and shocked that such a sound could come from a dying man.

My mum said, 'Oh, no,' then stood up and put her hands on my dad's shoulders. My dad let out another roar and I immediately stood up and looked around, as if his noise had awoken an old instinct in me. But I didn't know what to do.

My dad then pulled down his mask until it flapped round his neck. He held out his arms as if begging to someone and he screamed, 'Lazarus, Lazarus help me, help me Lazarus – oh God, no, don't, no . . . Lazarus help me, help me!' He cried to someone only he could see. He tried to stand but my mum kept him pressed to his seat.

'Draw the curtains,' my mum shouted to me. I was mesmerized by my dad. I stared at him wondering where he was.

'The curtains,' my mum insisted. I fumbled around and pulled the curtain round the bed space. The curtains were lurid orange and brown swirls. As I pulled them around us the light changed and we were enveloped by an orange glow.

'Lazarus!' my dad screamed again. 'Come . . . Lazarus, help me, oh it hurts, it hurts.'

For a moment it seemed like he was talking to me. He looked at me. 'It hurts, help me,' he said. I went to answer him, but then his eyes glazed and he screamed, 'Lazarus!' again.

'Shall I get the nurse?' I asked.

'No, she can hear,' my mum said.

My dad leant back in his chair and my mum let go of his shoulders. He sat panting, fast and furious, mouth open like a dog. My mum put the mask back over his mouth. As she sat back in her chair, my dad bounced and stood upright. He lifted up his nightshirt and began to tug at the tube which was dangling out of the end of his penis.

'Dad, don't!' I yelled.

'Get it out, get it out! Lazarus, help me get it out! It hurts, Lazarus! Oh God! Oh God! Help me!' he screamed. I grabbed at his hands and held them back. The strength of them surprised me. It was like arm-wrestling and I clenched my teeth with the effort of holding on to the grip.

My mum was up again trying to push my dad down on to his seat, but he wouldn't sit. Tears were in his eyes and falling down his cheeks.

'Oh God, Lazarus, please help me! Help me, please! No! No! Help me, please!'

We held on to him, then felt his body go limp as he collapsed back into his chair like an old rag doll. I pulled the nightshirt back over his genitals. He was quiet, but his eyes stayed wide, black with pupils, like a wild animal stalking prey.

'He's in pain,' my mum said.

'Have they given him anything?' I said. I was surprised to find I was out of breath. I panted, too.

'I don't know if he took it. It's not working anyway,' my mum said with contempt.

'I'll go and see,' I suggested, getting up from my seat. I parted the curtains and went into the white light of the ward. As I looked up I felt everyone's eyes on me. In our little tent you could believe you were alone. But on the other side you realized how everyone knew, everyone could hear, everyone could see our misery. Heads turned away as I looked round the ward. I heard a yell come from behind the curtain and I moved quickly away from it.

I found a nurse in the room where they sit.

'My dad seems to be in a lot of pain,' I said, going straight up to her, getting straight to the point. She stood with her back to me, replacing a file on a shelf. She turned quickly, startled.

'I'm sorry?' she asked.

'Mr Jacobs,' I said.

Her voice dropped. 'Oh.'

'He's in a lot of pain.'

'Well, we've tried to give him something, but he won't take it,' she said.

'What do you mean?'

'I tried to give him the pills but he just spat them out.'

'Pills,' I said. 'Why pills?'

'It's what's been prescribed.'

I took a breath to stay diplomatic. 'But he doesn't seem in any state to take pills. He's not all there. Can't he get an injection or something?'

'You'll have to see the doctor,' she said. 'She should be in in a minute.'

'I'll wait then,' I said, sitting down in a chair. The nurse turned back to the shelves. I could hear my dad crying out, horrible, moaning sobs. I wanted to put my fingers in my ears and hum to block out the sound, but the nurse's presence stopped me. As I listened to him scream, I began to get angry with him. An anger I could hardly bear to feel. Why couldn't he die gracefully, with dignity? Fading silently from life with a gentle smile and a touching last request. So his family could stand round his death bed and weep and mourn their loss. No, he had to die kicking and screaming, being pulled from life, being robbed. The loudest noise he had ever made in his life. The biggest protest. The first rail against injustice. Why now? Because he was going to die and he didn't want to go, he hadn't finished yet. Why now, when the pain and embarrassment could rob me of my grief?

'Can I help you?'

I looked up into a young woman's face. 'I'm the doctor here, for the ward. Can I help?'

'I hope so,' I said, gathering my thoughts. 'It's my dad, Mr Jacobs, he seems to be in a lot of pain. And that thing in his penis . . .'

'The catheter,' she said.

'Yes, whatever it's called, it seems to be hurting him. I mean, is it necessary?'

'His bladder is no longer functioning as it should – it sometimes happens to people in your father's state. We need to be able to draw off the liquid. It's uncomfortable, I know, but he would feel worse without it,' she said.

'I see, it's just that the nurse said she couldn't get him to take pain relief, because he wouldn't swallow the pills.'

'Yes, he spat them out,' she said.

'Well . . . couldn't he be given an injection instead?'

'He was put on pills,' she said, 'but I'll see what I can

243

do. I suppose it would make more sense.' She looked at me and smiled. As she did my dad gave out another loud 'Lazarus!' She turned her head in the direction of the noise.

'Isn't there anywhere else we can put him that is more private?' I asked.

'If there was I would have, believe me. It's not good to have that commotion on a ward – it disturbs everyone.'

'There must be something you can do,' I pleaded.

She sighed. 'I think it would be better for him if he went to a hospice. They'd be able to control the pain better than we can here.' She said it tentatively, as if to broach the subject with me, as if I'd be shocked by her suggestion.

'Yes! yes!' I said without hesitation. 'Can you do that?'

'Of course – I'll have to wait until tomorrow now – it's too late today, but I'll have him transferred tomorrow.'

I stared at her. That was it. 'I'll have him transferred tomorrow.' It could have been that easy. I could have asked the hospital all along. But I didn't know. I did not have that information. I had to stumble over it – come across it lying embedded in a conversation. I was led to believe . . . I was made to think . . . I was wrong. My good intentions were taking us the scenic route through his death.

'Are you all right?' I heard the doctor say. I went to speak, but nothing came out of my mouth.

'I'll see what I can do about the drugs, if you can just try and keep your father quiet.' She left the room.

I walked back up the ward. The orange and brown psychedelic curtains seemed an odd choice for a cancer ward. Probably chosen in the late sixties when they would have seemed subdued, there to cheer us all up. I parted them and entered the orange thrall.

My dad was sitting with his nightshirt up round his waist. My mum looked at me and as she went to speak, my dad screamed out, 'Help me, oh God!'

'Sschh, Dad!' my mum said, flicking her hand at him. She noticed his nightshirt and began to pull it back over his indecency.

'Oh God!' he shouted.

'Sschh, Dad.' I could hear the irritation in her voice, but she smiled at him as if he was a child doing something naughty but funny.

'What did they say?' she said, looking at me.

'She said she'll have him transferred to a hospice tomorrow.'

'What about the pain – did you ask them?'

'She said they tried to give him some pills.'

'I know, he spat them out. I said it's no good – they should give him an injection.'

'Lazarus!' My mum held on to my dad's knees to stop him standing.

'I said they should give him an injection but they take no notice. What good's pills? He spat them on the floor. He can't swallow – look at him.'

I didn't need to look, he was all around me.

'She's going to see if she can give him an injection,' I said.

My mum sucked her teeth long and loud. She rolled her eyes, then looked back towards my dad.

The curtains parted suddenly and the nurse stepped into the light. She was carrying a silver kidney-shaped bowl with a syringe on it.

'What's all this noise, Mr Jacobs?' she said loudly, shattering the atmosphere in the tent.

'Lazarus!' my dad shouted.

'Who's this Lazarus you want, Mr Jacobs – who is it? Would you like to wait outside,' she said to my mum and me. My mum smiled and we walked through the curtain to the exposure of the other side.

After a few minutes the nurse pulled back the curtain. My dad was revealed sitting neatly in his chair, his nightshirt

245

where it should be and his mask on his face. His eyes were shut and he was quiet.

'There, all done,' she said. 'I've given him something, for the pain.'

She picked up the clipboard from the edge of the bed, checked her watch then wrote something on the board. She clicked her pen off, then replaced the clipboard.

My mum and me sat down again in our places, but we crouched, waiting for my dad to erupt. He just sat inhaling with wheezing repetition. He didn't see us. He didn't know we were there.

My dad kept his eyes shut and looked as if he might be asleep.

'We might as well go, Ange,' my mum said. 'I'll get a lift with you. There's nothing much we can do here.'

The hospital phoned my mum that night. They said that she should come if she wanted to see my dad before 'he went'. I drove to her house, slowly – it was dark and rainy, I said to myself. But I didn't want to get to the hospital 'in time'. I wanted to let him go now. I didn't want any more memory of him like that – I'd got enough. I wanted him dead. I wished him dead.

As we walked down the ward I could see the curtains were drawn round his bed. I was scared they would be flung back at any moment and the fat, wild-eyed man would scream for Lazarus. But a nurse came out from inside the curtains carrying a silver kidney-shaped bowl. She looked at my mum, shook her head and gave a sympathetic smile.

'Mrs Jacobs, I'm afraid you're too late. He passed away about ten minutes ago. I'm sorry,' she said.

My mum nodded and smiled. I wanted to jump in the air and clap my hands. It was over, it was finally over, for him and for us. The loss of life that really happened weeks ago had finally ended.

'It was quite peaceful at the end,' the nurse went on. 'He just sort of fell asleep – he wasn't in pain.'

'Oh, thank you, Nurse,' my mum said.

We were both fixed to the spot, not knowing where to go next. The nurse looked embarrassed and searched for something else to say.

'The rabbi was with him at the end,' she said.

'The rabbi?' I asked.

'Yes, he managed to get here just in time. It took a long time to find one,' she said.

'Why a rabbi?'

The nurse looked confused. 'He is Jewish, isn't he?'

'No, he's not Jewish.'

'No, he's C of E,' my mum said.

The nurse's face moved through red to scarlet. She bit her lip. 'I'm sorry, we thought with his name and the way he . . .' she stopped herself and began again. 'I'm sorry, we thought he was Jewish.'

'No, he's C of E,' my mum repeated.

The nurse looked as if she might cry.

'Don't worry,' my mum said. 'I don't suppose he minded. At least someone was with him. Can I see him?'

The nurse parted the curtain for my mum, then she looked at me and said, 'I'm sorry about the rabbi,' as she walked off.

I walked into the orange glow once more. There was my dad, lying down. He was neat and symmetrical, arms by his side. His eyes were closed, but his mouth slightly open. His hair was splayed on the pillow like a mad professor's. And he was still. Inanimate.

My mum sat by his head. She put her hand on his forehead. 'He's still warm – he's still warm,' she said. She leant down to his ear and said, 'Dad, Dad,' quietly into it.

'He's dead, Mum,' I said softly.

'I know, I know – it's just that he's still warm. It doesn't seem right if he's still warm.'

I sat on the other side of the bed and laid my hand on top of his. His hand that I always held to cross the road.

'They got you a rabbi, Dad,' I said. 'God knows where you'll be now,' I smiled.

My mum put her hand on his forehead again. She watched his chest, then said to me, 'Oh, but he must be gone – you know why, Ange? Because he couldn't be lying down for so long.' She looked down into his face and said, 'When it comes, it comes quick.'

Chapter 25

THE DEATH

'Willie's gone missing, Ange,' my mum said on the phone. 'Yer dad's gone to look for her,' my mum went on. 'She's ill you know. I think she's dying, that's why she's gone. She couldn't walk properly. She's old you know, Ange. Yer dad let her out the other morning. She was crying and carrying on so he let her out. But after she went he realized she wasn't well and he shouldn't have done it. But you know he loves that cat. She just have to ask him for something he'd give it.

'She didn't come back that evening, so yer dad took a torch and went to look for her. He went to the park and he found her, but she was in the middle of one of those long pipes. You know the ones, the old sewer or something like that. He said he called her and called her, but she wouldn't come. He was gone for hours. Then he came back to get her some food. He thought she'd come because she'd be hungry. He took it back to the pipe but she still wouldn't come. He gave up eventually, came home with the saucer of food. He was so upset, Ange. He kept saying he shouldn't have let her out, he should have known. I said what's done's done. But he was so upset. You know, Ange, he cried. I've never seen your dad cry, not even when his brother die. But he loves that cat.

'You know, since you all left, they've been good friends. He'd feed her and play with her. And she was always round him, always ran to him – more than she did to me. Slept on his lap, like she was with you when you were younger. He loves that cat. He said she talked to him, you know, in her way. She understood what he said.

'Anyway, he's gone out to look again today. He's taken the day off work just to look for her. He says even if he just finds her body, at least he could give her a decent burial. Says he can't stand the thought of her being eaten or chased or something nasty happening to her.

'I've never seen him so upset. He really loves that cat. He's going to miss her. He said he'd never have another one because you just get attached to them and they die. I think she's dead, Ange – went somewhere to die. But I didn't say that to yer dad. He's too upset. He loves that cat. I hope he finds her.'